EP

Verbal Reasoning

& Comprehension

The 11+

10-Minute Tests

For the CEM (Durham University) test

Book 2

Ages
10-11

Practise • Prepare • Pass

Everything your child needs for 11+ success

How to use this book

This book is made up of 10-minute tests and puzzle pages.
There are answers and detailed explanations in the pull-out section at the back of the book.

10-Minute Tests

*   There are 32 tests in this book, each containing either 20 or 26 questions.

*   Each test is designed to cover a good range of the question styles and topics that your child could see in the verbal reasoning section of their 11+ test, at the same difficulty level.

*   Your child should aim to score around 17 out of 20 or 22 out of 26 in each of the 10-minute tests. If they score less than this, use their results to work out the areas they need more practice on.

*   If your child hasn't managed to finish the test in time, they need to work on increasing their speed, whereas if they have made a lot of mistakes, they need to work more carefully.

*   Keep track of your child's scores using the progress chart on the inside back cover of the book.

Puzzle Pages

*   There are 6 puzzle pages in this book. The puzzles are a great break from test preparation. They also encourage children to practise the same skills that they will need in the test, but in a fun way.

Published by CGP

Editors:
Emma Cleasby, Jack Perry, Sophie Scott

With thanks to Holly Robinson and Alison Griffin for the proofreading.

Please note that CGP is not associated with CEM or The University of Durham in any way.
This book does not include any official questions and it is not endorsed by CEM or The University of Durham.
CEM, Centre for Evaluation and Monitoring, Durham University and *The University of Durham*
are all trademarks of The University of Durham.

ISBN: 978 1 78294 766 0
Printed by Elanders Ltd, Newcastle upon Tyne
Clipart from Corel®

Based on the classic CGP style created by Richard Parsons.

Contents

You have **10 minutes** to do this test. Work as quickly and as accurately as you can.

Read this poem carefully and answer the questions that follow.

To A Usurper*

Aha! a traitor in the camp,
　A rebel strangely bold,—
A lisping, laughing, toddling scamp,
　Not more than four years old!

5　To think that I, who've ruled alone
　So proudly in the past,
Should be ejected from my throne
　By my own son at last!

He trots his treason to and fro,
10　As only babies can,
And says he'll be his mamma's beau**
　When he's a "gweat, big man"!

You stingy boy! you've always had
　A share in mamma's heart;
15　Would you begrudge your poor old dad
　The tiniest little part?

That mamma, I regret to see,
　Inclines to take your part,—
As if a dual monarchy***
20　Should rule her gentle heart!

But when the years of youth have sped,
　The bearded man, I trow****,
Will quite forget he ever said
　He'd be his mamma's beau.

25　Renounce your treason, little son,
　Leave mamma's heart to me;
For there will come another one
　To claim your loyalty.

And when that other comes to you,
30　God grant her love may shine
Through all your life, as fair and true
　As mamma's does through mine!

Eugene Field

* usurper — *someone who wrongfully takes the place of another.*
　　　Here, it's used by a father who is addressing his son.
** beau — *a sweetheart*
*** dual monarchy — *here, a monarchy in which there are two rulers.*
**** trow — *think*

Answer these questions about the text that you've just read.
Circle the letter that matches the correct answer.

1. Why does the father call his son a "traitor" (line 1)?

    A   His son has betrayed the family.

    B   His son has taken his kingdom away from him.

    C   He thinks his son is taking his place in the mother's heart.

    D   He knows his son won't love his mother as much when he grows up.

2. Which of these statements best describes the age of the "traitor"?

    A   He is a teenager.

    B   He is an adult.

    C   He is a newborn baby.

    D   He is a young child.

3. Which of these statements is false?

    A   The son is vocal about his love for his mother.

    B   The mother intends on staying loyal to the father alone.

    C   The father wants at least some of the mother's heart.

    D   The father was once the sole ruler of the mother's heart.

4. What does the word "stingy" (line 13) mean?

    A   Ungenerous

    B   Tiresome

    C   Small

    D   Domineering

5. Why does the writer use the word "gweat" in the phrase, "When he's a "gweat, big man"!" (line 12)?

   A   The father's pronunciation is wrong.

   B   The child is unable to spell.

   C   The father is mimicking how his son speaks.

   D   The son is using a nickname for his mother.

6. Which of these does not describe how the father feels?

   A   Jealous

   B   Upset

   C   Elated

   D   Affectionate

7. According to the text, what are the father's hopes for his son's future?

   A   He wants his son to face justice.

   B   He hopes his son finds true and lasting love.

   C   He wants his son to become religious.

   D   He wants his son to be happier than he has been.

Find the word that means the same, or nearly the same, as the word on the left.

    Example: **wide**   flat   straight   <u>broad</u>   long

---

8. **merit**   rewarded worthy deserve prized

9. **successor**   replace followers descendant winner

10. **fable**   fiction parable novel book

11. **wonder**   astonish marvel revelation miraculous

12. **balanced**   steady neutralise equality stability

13. **arrest**   thwarted apprehend imprisons captive

Mark the word outside the brackets that has a similar meaning to the words in both sets of brackets.

Example: (twig branch) (fasten attach)   glue <u>stick</u> affix bough

14. (redden blush)   (hue tinge)   crimson colour flush shade

15. (regular habitual)   (procedure regimen)   pattern plan standard routine

16. (peal strike)   (fee levy)   charge toll resound tithe

17. (tilt incline)   (inventory record)   ramp catalogue list tally

18. (wedge stick)   (gatehouse cottage)   cabin jam catch lodge

19. (book secure)   (store stockpile)   confirm cache reserve pool

20. (caustic hurtful)   (piece snippet)   scathing bit trimming cutting

END OF TEST

/ 20

You have **10 minutes** to do this test. Work as quickly and as accurately as you can.

Fill in the missing letters to complete the words in the following passage.

1. Motion capture involves using c a ☐ e ☐ a s and specially designed

2. markers to record real-life ☐ o v ☐ m ☐ n ☐ s and turn them into

3. data. This data can be r e ☐ ☐ by a computer, and even be made into

    an on-screen image.

4. This motion capture t ☐ c h n ☐ l ☐ g ☐ is employed in a

5. r a ☐ g ☐ of different ways. For example, scientists have used motion

6. capture to improve their k ☐ o ☐ l ☐ ☐ g e of the ways in which

7. ☐ u m ☐ ☐ s and animals walk and run; this is called gait analysis.

8. Engineers often use motion capture to create r e ☐ ☐ l i ☐ t i ☐

9. visualisations of their d ☐ s i ☐ n s.

10. Arguably the most ☐ r e a ☐ i v ☐ utilisation of this

    increasingly sophisticated technology can be found in the film and television

11. i n ☐ u ☐ t r ☐ e s, where motion capture is often used to

12. ☐ n i ☐ a t e and bring to life complex computer-generated

    characters and environments.

Three of the words in each list are linked. Mark the word that is not related to these three.

Example: journal   diary   <u>textbook</u>   notebook

13. cheese   butter   egg   milk

14. laughable   whimsical   comical   risible

15. hosepipe   bucket   jug   beaker

16. extra   auxiliary   additional   vital

17. timber   plank   rafter   crate

Complete the word on the right so that it means the same, or nearly the same, as the word on the left.

Example: scared   [a][f][r][a][i][d]

18. speak   [v][o][c][ ][l][ ][ ][e]

19. skittish   [ ][x][ ][i][t][ ][b][l][e]

20. desire   [ ][o][v][ ][t]

21. deceit   [ ][i][s][ ][o][n][ ][s][ ][y]

22. poor   [d][e][ ][t][ ][ ][u][ ][e]

In each question below, the words can be rearranged to form a sentence. One word doesn't fit in the sentence. Underline the word that doesn't fit.

Example: red   the   has   <u>ride</u>   girl   bicycle   a

23. brother   school   me   followed   yesterday   little   my   walked   with   to

24. bonnet   start   on   the   car   so   he   wouldn't   looked   the   under

25. destination   them   took   for   their   get   it   time   reach   long   to   a

26. very   mountain   scaling   be   proved   an   task   the   to   arduous

END OF TEST

/ 26

You have **10 minutes** to do this test. Work as quickly and as accurately as you can.

Read this passage carefully and answer the questions that follow.

The Burj Khalifa

For many centuries, the world's tallest buildings were grand European churches. However, the early 20th century saw a new contender — the skyscraper. Since 1998, Malaysia and Taiwan have successively laid claim to the world's tallest skyscraper, a record formerly held exclusively by the USA. However, perhaps the most imposing
5 skyscraper to date is the impressive Burj Khalifa in the UAE in western Asia.

The Burj Khalifa is a mixed-purpose tower that has officially held the record for the tallest building on earth since 2009. Built over five years using more than 4,000 tonnes of steel, this imposing tower is glazed almost entirely in crystal-clear windows. It looms over the city of Dubai, reaching a stunning height of 828 metres. The concrete
10 foundations and first 100 floors of the structure were finished in just under three years.

Among other functions, the tower's 163 usable overground floors include office spaces, a luxury hotel and various residential units (the highest of which is at dizzying heights on the 108th floor). Built by an international team of architects, the Burj Khalifa's interior design features luxurious materials from around the globe.

15 The Burj Khalifa is associated with several world records. Visitors can travel to the 148th floor to experience incredible views from what, until 2015, was the world's highest observation deck. Thrill-seekers, lured by the tower's breathtaking altitude, secured the record for the highest BASE jump from a building in 2014. The tower also presents a challenge for climbers, providing the world's highest building climb. Alain
20 Roberts, known as the 'Human Spider', scaled the tower in about six hours in 2011.

The Burj Khalifa is soon set to be overshadowed by several new immensely tall skyscrapers. Both the Jeddah Tower in Saudi Arabia, due to be finished by 2020, and the Burj Mubarak al-Kabir in Kuwait will be over one kilometre tall once completed — the latter is still in its planning stages. Even these titanic buildings will be overtaken
25 if the ambitious design of Japan's proposed Sky Mile Tower is realised, though this mile-high colossus would not be completed until the 2040s.

Answer these questions about the text that you've just read.
Circle the letter that matches the correct answer.

1. According to the text, which of these countries has not been home the world's tallest skyscraper?

   A   Kuwait

   B   UAE

   C   Taiwan

   D   USA

2. According to the text, which of these statements about the Burj Khalifa must be true?

   A   It took more than five years to build.

   B   The lead architect for the project came from America.

   C   The members of the construction team all came from the UAE.

   D   The 100th floor was finished at least two years before construction ended.

3. According to the text, which of these statements must be false?

   A   More floors of the Burj Khalifa are dedicated to a hotel than office space.

   B   Only the first ten floors of the Burj Khalifa are open to the public.

   C   Property prices in the Burj Khalifa are some of the highest in the world.

   D   Nobody permanently lives on the 115th floor.

4. Which of these materials is not an essential part of the Burj Khalifa's structure?

   A   Concrete

   B   Crystal

   C   Steel

   D   Glass

5. Which of the following best describes the main purpose of the Burj Khalifa?

   A　　To break world records.

   B　　To give visitors a vantage point over Dubai.

   C　　To provide space for residential and commercial purposes.

   D　　To provide apartments for various residents.

6. Which of the following achievements was not associated with the Burj Khalifa in 2016?

   A　　Highest unassisted climb of a building.

   B　　Tallest man-made structure.

   C　　Highest observation deck.

   D　　Highest BASE jump from a building.

7. Why is the Burj Khalifa expected to soon lose its status as the world's tallest building?

   A　　Japan is in the process of building the Sky Mile Tower.

   B　　The Jeddah Tower will be taller than the Burj Khalifa before its completion.

   C　　It will lose its status once the Burj Mubarak al-Kabir has been built.

   D　　Every skyscraper will be taller than the Burj Khalifa in the future.

Mark the word outside the brackets that has a similar meaning to the words in both sets of brackets.

Example: (twig　branch)　(fasten　attach)　　glue <u>stick</u> affix bough

---

8.　(upright decent)　(lesson message)　　　erect moral example class

9.　(strum pick)　　(courage daring)　　　mettle nerve twang pluck

10. (assistance aid)　(amenity facility)　　favour help service provision

11. (colonise occupy)   (pacify subdue)   inhabit settle invade calm

12. (radical drastic)   (farthest outermost)   utmost fringe extreme edge

13. (transfer distribute)   (save rescue)   deliver yield entrust convey

14. (assortment mixture)   (oven stove)   array range cooker set

In each question below, the words can be rearranged to form a sentence. One word doesn't fit in the sentence. Underline the word that doesn't fit.

Example: red the has <u>ride</u> girl bicycle a

15. tickets quickly not film sold very the for out the

16. happiest would vet the my dog had seen ever the was

17. cake top with nice raspberries a he strawberry made on icing

18. decided the to house different they move after holidays

19. had I leaf tree many climbed up oak an branches that

20. picks school Fridays dad his from on him every up

END OF TEST

/ 20

You have **10 minutes** to do this test. Work as quickly and as accurately as you can.

Choose the correct words to complete the passage below.

The life of the astronomer Caroline Herschel is often

1. ☐ alike
   ☐ compare
   ☐ likened
   ☐ similar

to that of Cinderella.

2. ☐ at
   ☐ on
   ☐ in
   ☐ over

Born ⎡   ⎤ Hanover in 1750, Caroline spent her childhood doing domestic chores.

She received a

3. ☐ interesting
   ☐ rudimentary
   ☐ kind
   ☐ simply

education from her father, but she was not expected to

marry and seemed

4. ☐ destined
   ☐ appointed
   ☐ designed
   ☐ reserved

to become a servant. However, she moved to England

to be with her brother, William, where she

5. ☐ worked
   ☐ managed
   ☐ lived
   ☐ reigned

his household and learnt to

sing. The siblings pursued a musical

6. ☐ jobs
   ☐ career
   ☐ groups
   ☐ show

before William's increasing interest in the

stars prompted the

7. ☐ pair
   ☐ double
   ☐ dual
   ☐ trio

to devote more time to astronomy. At first, Caroline just

8.
- ☐ jot
- ☐ took
- ☐ noted
- ☐ writing

assisted William, **[8]** down his observations, but she

9.
- ☐ lately
- ☐ soon
- ☐ after
- ☐ to

[9] developed

10.
- ☐ love
- ☐ knowledge
- ☐ affinity
- ☐ interest

her own **[10]** in astronomy, after which she discovered several comets and

11.
- ☐ money
- ☐ income
- ☐ salary
- ☐ funding

compiled a complex catalogue of stars. In 1787, the king gave Caroline a **[11]**,

12.
- ☐ contribution
- ☐ profession
- ☐ work
- ☐ abilities

making her one of the first women to be paid for her **[12]** to science.

Complete the word on the right so that it means the opposite, or nearly the opposite, as the word on the left.

Example: heavy | l | i | g | h | t |

13. typical | a | | n | o | | m | a | |

14. foreign | | n | d | i | | e | | o | u | s |

15. isolated | a | c | | e | | | i | b | l | |

16. plain | o | | n | | t | |

Mark the word outside the brackets that has a similar meaning to the words in both sets of brackets.

Example: (twig   branch)   (fasten   attach)   glue <u>stick</u> affix bough

17. (swap   exchange)   (profession   craft)   occupation trade barter job

18. (whole   intact)   (finished   fulfilled)   done entire complete unabridged

19. (pledge   oath)   (potential   aptitude)   vow assurance capacity promise

20. (situation   incident)   (material   substance)   matter medium fabric business

21. (caution   heed)   (foster   nurse)   concern watch care custody

Complete the word on the right so that it means the same, or nearly the same, as the word on the left.

Example: scared [a][f][r][a][i][d]

22. copy   [d][ ][p][l][ ][ ][a][t][e]

23. blaze   [i][ ][ ][e][r][ ][o]

24. attack   [ ][s][s][a][ ][l][ ]

25. lessen   [d][ ][m][ ][n][i][ ][h]

26. savage   [ ][a][ ][b][a][r][ ][c]

END OF TEST

/ 26

15

You have **10 minutes** to do this test. Work as quickly and as accurately as you can.

Read this passage carefully and answer the questions that follow.

The Door

Throwing herself over the gate, Liv headed into the field and increased her pace, despite the stitch in her side and the heavy school books rattling in her rucksack.

"Come on, Max!" Liv shouted encouragingly to her little brother. Even though they'd skipped breakfast altogether, they'd still need to race through their familiar
5 shortcut if they were to make it to registration on time.

"I'm going as fast as I can," yelled Max breathlessly, struggling to catch up.

Liv was halfway across the field when a wave of cacophonous sounds erupted around her, shattering the early morning quiet. A fearsome, whirling gust of wind howled all around the countryside, forcing Liv to the ground. Then, the thunderous
10 wind cut out instantly, leaving a deathly silence in its wake.

In the calm, Liv leapt to her feet. "Max?" she cried. She wheeled around, but the figure of the small boy was nowhere to be seen. She stumbled through the damp grass, hoping that he was close by. Scrambling to retrace her steps, she breathed a sigh of relief as she saw her brother. He was lying in the grass and quite unharmed,
15 looking towards the gate that they had just left behind.

"Liv! You need to see this."

Liv's gaze was immediately drawn to the far side of the field where Max was pointing, mouth wide with amazement. Where a fence had been before, there now stood a great, wooden door.

20 Liv's fear began to dissipate. The appearance of the door was certainly curious and frightening, but she had been preparing to face a great demon or an army of monstrous creatures. The door's solid oak beams and iron bars seemed mundane in comparison.

"Can we open it?" asked Max excitedly.

25 Liv hesitated. For a second, the door seemed to shimmer, as if it were about to fade back into oblivion. A strong sense of foreboding took hold of Liv, yet she felt compelled to stride up to the door and grasp its heavy, iron handle.

16

1. Which of the following statements must be true?

    A   The field provides a faster way to school than other routes.

    B   Liv and Max frequently have running races in the field.

    C   Liv knows the way across the field, but Max doesn't.

    D   Liv and Max only cross the field when they are late for registration.

2. What does the word "cacophonous" (line 7) mean?

    A   Loud

    B   Horrible

    C   Discordant

    D   Confusing

3. What evidence is there that Liv cares for Max?

    A   She shouts encouragingly to him to hurry up.

    B   She leads the way for Max across the field.

    C   She is relieved to find him after she is knocked over by the strange wind.

    D   She opens the door when Max asks her to.

4. Why does Liv's fear begin to "dissipate" in line 20?

    A   She realises that Max is unharmed.

    B   She thought that the wind had brought something scarier than the door.

    C   The noise and the wind have disappeared.

    D   She doesn't find the door scary.

5. How do Max and Liv react to the door?

    A   Max doesn't want Liv to open the door.

    B   Max finds the door less interesting than Liv.

    C   Max doesn't want to open the door as much as Liv does.

    D   Liv is more wary of the door than Max.

6. According to the text, "A strong sense of foreboding took hold of Liv" (line 26). What does this tell you?

    A   Liv doesn't know what is on the other side of the door.

    B   Liv is just as scared as she was before she saw the door.

    C   Liv is no longer afraid.

    D   Liv is starting to worry about what might happen next.

7. Which of the following best describes the nature of the door?

    A   Enthralling

    B   Boring

    C   Interesting

    D   Horrific

Three of the words in each list are linked. Mark the word that is not related to these three.

    Example: journal   diary   <u>textbook</u>   notebook

---

8.   hateful   virulent   despicable   heinous

9.   betray   entrap   denounce   deceive

10. wave   current   reef   tide

11. veterinarian   farmer   vegetarian   breeder

12. hobby   interest   pastime   relaxation

13. concrete   imaginary   physical   tangible

Find the word that means the same, or nearly the same, as the word on the left.

Example: **wide**   flat   straight   <u>broad</u>   long

---

14. **trembling**   tremors   rocking   excited   quivering

15. **magical**   spiritual   fantasy   supernatural   ghostly

16. **eaten**   consumed   sated   swallowed   digested

17. **dreadful**   depressing   alarmed   terror   grievous

18. **fraction**   divisive   portion   parts   fragmented

19. **fund**   sponsorship   supporter   bank   finance

20. **agreement**   according   united   concord   consented

END OF TEST

/ 20

Time for a break! This puzzle is a great way to practise your **vocabulary** skills.

Monster Mutiny

Captain Monster's crew are hiding from him on different ships in the fleet. Use the clues below to work out which ship each crew member is on. Write their names under the correct ship.

Stan
Let me tell you
Which ship to select,
It's the one named with
An antonym of protect.

Bill
If you wish
To uncover me,
Search the ship
That means jeopardy.

Lizzie
The ship in which
I lie in wait,
Is a synonym
Of irate.

Alice
The ship that means
Aggressive and robust,
Is the one in which
You should place your trust.

Marco
It certainly wouldn't
Be a waste of time,
If you searched the ship that
Means secure and chime.

Furious

Vigorous

Sound

Peril

Endanger

_____

_____

_____

_____

_____

You have **10 minutes** to do this test. Work as quickly and as accurately as you can.

Fill in the missing letters to complete the words in the following passage.

1. S [ ] t [ ] a [ ] e [ ] on the banks of the River Thames is one of

2. London's most r e [ ] o [ ] [ ] i s [ ] b l e landmarks.

3. At 135 metres high, the London Eye is a [ ] t r [ ] k i n [ ] feature

4. of the London [ ] k y [ ] [ ] n e and one of the world's largest

    Ferris wheels.

5. The London Eye was constructed to c [ ] m m [ ] m o [ ] [ ] t e

    the start of the new millennium. It was originally intended to be a

6. t [ ] m p [ ] r [ ] [ ] y structure and, when it was built, there were

7. already plans to d i [ ] m a n [ ] [ ] e it after five years and move it to

8. a new l [ ] c [ ] t i [ ] n. However, since opening to the public in

9. 2000, m [ ] l l [ ] [ ] n s of tourists have ridden the Eye and it has

10. become one of the most p [ ] p [ ] l a [ ] attractions in the city.

    Each revolution of the Eye takes 30 minutes, and offers passengers

11. s [ ] e [ ] t a c [ ] [ ] a r views over London. On a clear day,

    you can see as far as Windsor Castle, almost forty

12. k [ ] l o [ ] e t [ ] [ ] s away.

21

Complete the word on the right so that it means the opposite, or nearly the opposite, of the word on the left.

Example: heavy l i g h t

13. hide   ⬜ x p ⬜ s e

14. constant   v a ⬜ i ⬜ b ⬜ e

15. hesitant   ⬜ e c i ⬜ v e

16. avoid   ⬜ o n f ⬜ ⬜ ⬜ t

17. important   t ⬜ i ⬜ i a ⬜

Three of the words in each list are linked. Mark the word that is not related to these three.

Example: journal   diary   <u>textbook</u>   notebook

18. verdict   result   forecast   judgement

19. inscribe   scribble   scrawl   jot

20. assistance   advancement   promotion   upgrade

21. scarf   cravat   bangle   necklace

22. persistent   tenacious   unwavering   irresolute

In each question below, the words can be rearranged to form a sentence. One word doesn't fit in the sentence. Underline the word that doesn't fit.

Example: red   the   has   <u>ride</u>   girl   bicycle   a

23. can   complete   is   sleep   when   only   I   there   noise   silence

24. didn't   knew   the   where   nobody   was   hiding   dog

25. rocking   fifty   age   is   chair   years   over   old   the

26. didn't   final   for   manage   failed   the   he   to   round   qualify

END OF TEST

/ 26

You have **10 minutes** to do this test. Work as quickly and as accurately as you can.

Read this passage carefully and answer the questions that follow.

Yosemite National Park

In a world of ever-expanding cities, national parks offer respite from the hubbub of the modern world. There are over 400 national parks in Europe, and many more worldwide, all helping to preserve areas of natural beauty and conserve wildlife.

5   Yosemite National Park, founded in 1890, is one of America's most famous national parks, encompassing over 700,000 acres of unspoilt forests and mountains. These mountains include the iconic Half Dome and El Capitan, which is known worldwide for its many tricky climbing routes, including the sheer Dawn Wall route. The two mountains stand at 2,694 metres and 2,308 metres respectively.

Before Yosemite became a national park, sheep and cattle grazed there, which
10   devastated its forests. This destruction caught the attention of the naturalist John Muir. Born in Scotland in 1838, Muir moved to America with his family when he was 11. He loved the natural world and wrote articles arguing that Yosemite should be turned into a national park. He was so influential that the American government made Yosemite a national park just a year after his campaign began.

15   Before his death in 1914, Muir was visited by President Theodore Roosevelt, whom he convinced to become a champion of national parks. In 1915, shortly after Muir's death, a 211-mile hiking trail through Yosemite began construction. This trail would become known as the 'John Muir Trail', in honour of the naturalist. The trail was completed 23 years later, during a special year for fans of Yosemite and the late John Muir.

20   Today, Yosemite National Park is popular with tourists, who come to admire the breathtaking scenery. The mountainous area also makes Yosemite a favourite for rock climbers from across the world. In January 2015, natives Tommy Caldwell and Kevin Jorgeson became the first to free-climb the Dawn Wall route, taking 19 days to complete their ascent. In November 2016, a Czech climber called Adam Ondra beat
25   their record by free-climbing the same route in less than half the time.

Answer these questions about the text that you've just read.
Circle the letter that matches the correct answer.

1. What are national parks?

    A   Areas of cities and towns that are particularly busy.

    B   Areas of countryside that are protected by the government.

    C   Areas that can only be found in Europe.

    D   Areas that contain lots of interesting wildlife.

2. In what year did John Muir begin campaigning to make Yosemite a national park?

    A   1838

    B   1849

    C   1889

    D   1890

3. Which of the following does the text not attribute to John Muir?

    A   Discovering the route for the John Muir Trail through Yosemite.

    B   Persuading the government to make Yosemite a national park.

    C   Inspiring President Roosevelt to promote national parks.

    D   Noticing the destruction caused by sheep and cattle farming in Yosemite.

4. What is special about the year that the John Muir Trail was completed?

    A   It is 25 years after the death of John Muir.

    B   It is 50 years after the founding of Yosemite National Park.

    C   It is 75 years after Theodore Roosevelt visited Muir in Yosemite.

    D   It is 100 years after the birth of John Muir.

5. According to the text, which of the following must be true?

   A   The record free-climb of the Dawn Wall route was completed in 7 days.

   B   The Dawn Wall route is the hardest climbing route up El Capitan.

   C   El Capitan is attractive to climbers because it is shorter than Half Dome.

   D   Ondra's free-climb of the Dawn Wall route took place
       within two years of its first successful free-climb.

6. According to the text, which of the following must be false?

   A   Theodore Roosevelt visited Yosemite before it had become a national park.

   B   Kevin Jorgeson is a famous European climber.

   C   Tommy Caldwell is one of only three climbers to free-climb El Capitan.

   D   John Muir's interest in nature began in Scotland.

7. What did John Muir and Adam Ondra have in common?

   A   They both set world records.

   B   They were both passionate about conservation in Yosemite.

   C   They were both born outside of America.

   D   They both met Theodore Roosevelt.

Find the word that means the same, or nearly the same, as the word on the left.

   Example: **wide**   flat   straight   <u>broad</u>   long

---

8. **real**   spurious   potent   authentic   valid

9. **guide**   command   shepherd   ease   promote

10. **chaos**   disarray   untidy   disturbance   instability

11. **invade**   engulf   breach   troop   sequestrate

12. **wordy**   verbose   pompous   boastful   pithy

13. **concern**   repentance   anxiety   discompose   torment

14. **discard**   vacate   jettison   misplace   refuse

Three of the words in each list are linked. Mark the word that is not related to these three.

Example: journal   diary   <u>textbook</u>   notebook

15. drum   guitar   piano   brass

16. fuel   power   charge   engine

17. translucent   clear   simple   straightforward

18. sage   parsley   salt   rosemary

19. lung   muscle   heart   stomach

20. edge   verge   column   periphery

END OF TEST

/ 20

Test 8

You have **10 minutes** to do this test. Work as quickly and as accurately as you can.

Choose the correct words to complete the passage below.

Many people choose to holiday abroad,

1. ☐ trading
    ☐ prefer
    ☐ alternating
    ☐ picking

the cold British

rain for hot, foreign sunshine. However, 'staycations' have been increasing in

2. ☐ popular
    ☐ popularity
    ☐ favoured
    ☐ approval

over the

3. ☐ recent
    ☐ passed
    ☐ past
    ☐ former

few years. Studies show that the number

of Britons choosing to

4. ☐ travels
    ☐ holiday
    ☐ break
    ☐ rest

in the UK has been rising

5. ☐ before
    ☐ around
    ☐ since
    ☐ about

2008,

and the upward trend is

6. ☐ exacerbating
    ☐ continuing
    ☐ pursuing
    ☐ extending

.

There are many advantages to a 'staycation', with

7. ☐ most
    ☐ majority
    ☐ best
    ☐ group

people opting for a

local holiday for financial

8. ☐ points
    ☐ comforts
    ☐ reasons
    ☐ excuses

. Reduced travel times, familiar foods

28

and being able to avoid airports have

9. ☐ too
☐ besides
☐ also
☐ additional

been listed as motives for

choosing to stay

10. ☐ inside
☐ at home
☐ abroad
☐ indoors

. But it is not

11. ☐ just
☐ alone
☐ single
☐ exactly

holidaymakers who are

enjoying staycations. Many UK businesses

12. ☐ rest
☐ anticipate
☐ confident
☐ depend

on trade from tourism

and have seen increased profits in recent years.

Complete the word on the right so that it means the same, or nearly the same, as the word on the left.

Example: scared   [a][f][r][a][i][d]

13. wild   [u][ ][ ][m][e][d]

14. nasty   [h][ ][r][r][ ][b][l][ ]

15. answer   [ ][e][ ][p][ ][n][s][ ]

16. sanitise [d][ ][s][i][ ][f][e][ ][ ]

Mark the word outside the brackets that has a similar meaning to the words in both sets of brackets.

Example: (twig   branch)   (fasten   attach)   glue <u>stick</u> affix bough

17. (rush   raid)   (tempest   downpour)   onslaught   storm   gale   harry

18. (integer   digit)   (total   quantity)   item   whole   amount   number

19. (gesture   signal)   (ripple   tide)   sign   undulate   wave   flood

20. (study   poll)   (inspect   observe)   see   sample   question   survey

21. (collision   crash) (effect   aftermath)   impact   clash   result   knock

Three of the words in each list are linked. Mark the word that is not related to these three.

Example: journal   diary   <u>textbook</u>   notebook

22. singer   soloist   actor   vocalist

23. racket   bat   ball   club

24. juice   water   liquid   wine

25. illegal   immoral   unlawful   forbidden

26. cloth   fabric   towel   material

END OF TEST

/ 26

You have **10 minutes** to do this test. Work as quickly and as accurately as you can.

Read this passage carefully and answer the questions that follow.

An extract from 'Around the World in Eighty Days'

"We are going round the world."

Passepartout opened wide his eyes, raised his eyebrows, held up his hands, and seemed about to collapse, so overcome was he with stupefied astonishment.

"Round the world!" he murmured.

5   "In eighty days," responded Mr. Fogg. "So we haven't a moment to lose."

"But the trunks?" gasped Passepartout, unconsciously swaying his head from right to left.

"We'll have no trunks; only a carpet-bag, with two shirts and three pairs of stockings for me, and the same for you. We'll buy our clothes on the way. Bring down my

10 mackintosh and traveling-cloak, and some stout shoes, though we shall do little walking. Make haste!"

Passepartout tried to reply, but could not. He went out, mounted to his own room, fell into a chair, and muttered: "That's good, that is! And I, who wanted to remain quiet!"

He mechanically set about making the preparations for departure. Around the world

15 in eighty days! Was his master a fool? No. Was this a joke, then? They were going to Dover; good! To Calais; good again! After all, Passepartout, who had been away from France five years, would not be sorry to set foot on his native soil again. Perhaps they would go as far as Paris, and it would do his eyes good to see Paris once more. But surely a gentleman so chary* of his steps would stop there; no doubt — but, then, it was

20 none the less true that he was going away, this so domestic person hitherto**!

By eight o'clock Passepartout had packed the modest carpet-bag, containing the wardrobes of his master and himself; then, still troubled in mind, he carefully shut the door of his room, and descended to Mr. Fogg.

Jules Verne

* chary — *cautious*

** hitherto — *until now*

Answer these questions about the text that you've just read.
Circle the letter that matches the correct answer.

1. According to the text, which of the following best describes Passepartout's relationship to Mr. Fogg?

   A   He is Mr. Fogg's friend.

   B   He is Mr. Fogg's younger brother.

   C   He is Mr. Fogg's servant.

   D   He is Mr. Fogg's travelling partner.

2. What are Passepartout's expectations for the journey?

   A   They will go as far as Paris and no further.

   B   They will do a lot of walking.

   C   The journey won't go ahead as it's just a joke Mr. Fogg is playing.

   D   They will struggle with the language in France.

3. Why does Passepartout pack his clothes "mechanically" (line 14)?

   A   He uses a machine to pack his clothes.

   B   He has to work quickly to meet Mr. Fogg's deadline.

   C   He wants to make sure he does a good job.

   D   He is too busy thinking about what Mr. Fogg has said.

4. Passepartout describes Mr. Fogg as "this so domestic person hitherto" (line 20). What does this tell us about Mr. Fogg?

   A   He is very good at housework.

   B   It is unusual for him to want to travel.

   C   He is unpredictable.

   D   He is normally very impulsive.

5. Why does Mr. Fogg suggest they pack very few items?

   A   So they have plenty of space for packing souvenirs.

   B   They don't own any luggage that can fit large items.

   C   So they can leave quickly.

   D   So they can carry all of their luggage themselves.

6. By the end of the text, how does Passepartout feel?

   A   Apprehensive, but resigned.

   B   Enthusiastic, but circumspect.

   C   Distressed, but optimistic.

   D   Serene, but confused.

7. What does the word "stupefied" (line 3) mean?

   A   Idiotic

   B   Enchanted

   C   Stunned

   D   Frightened

Complete the word on the right so that it means the opposite, or nearly the opposite, of the word on the left.

Example: heavy   l i g h t

8. shortage   s _ r p _ _ s

9. cease   p _ r s _ _ t

10. obscure   _ l a _ _ f _

11. gentle   f ☐ r o ☐ i ☐ u s

12. deadly   b ☐ n i g ☐

13. predictable   ☐ r ☐ a t ☐ ☐

Mark the word outside the brackets that has a similar meaning to the words in both sets of brackets.

Example: (twig   branch)   (fasten   attach)   glue <u>stick</u> affix bough

14. (estuary   bay)   (divide   rift)   gap   chasm   gulf   abyss

15. (traverse   navigate) (angry   vexed)   irate   captious   negotiate   cross

16. (brook   tributary)   (surge   gush)   creek   rivulet   stream   cascade

17. (revolt   mutiny)   (turn   spin)   revolution   riot   wheel   orbit

18. (scowl   glower)   (dazzle   shine)   frown   leer   radiance   glare

19. (agreement   pact)   (shrink   reduce)   diminish   deal   contract   cut

20. (thrash   beat)   (staff   stick)   crook   cane   lash   whip

END OF TEST

/ 20

You have **10 minutes** to do this test. Work as quickly and as accurately as you can.

Choose the correct words to complete the passage below.

In modern Britain, people have come to

1. ☐ hope
☐ resist
☐ expect
☐ believe

gloomy winters that are more

2. ☐ probably
☐ possibly
☐ surely
☐ likely

to produce rain than ice and snow. However, this wasn't always the case.

At several points in British

3. ☐ account
☐ history
☐ background
☐ archive

, the temperatures were so

4. ☐ blistering
☐ glacial
☐ tepid
☐ clement

that London's River Thames froze over. On such occasions, the city's

5. ☐ fauna
☐ parents
☐ residents
☐ occupier

hosted frost fairs — festivals that sprang up on the

6. ☐ ice
☐ chilled
☐ frozen
☐ flowing

river. Londoners hosted

football

7. ☐ game
☐ matches
☐ teams
☐ spots

, markets and circuses

8. ☐ through
☐ beneath
☐ against
☐ atop

the thick ice.

The most

9. ☐ famous
☐ great
☐ pathetic
☐ forgettable

frost fair was held in the depths of the Great Frost of 1683-84.

Called the Blanket Fair, people came from far and

10. ☐ few
☐ from
☐ flung
☐ wide

to take part in horse races,

shows and much more on the frozen river. In

11. ☐ effect
☐ hindsight
☐ total
☐ aggregate

, seven frost fairs were held

between 1607 and 1814. After that,

12. ☐ more
☐ milder
☐ cooler
☐ increase

temperatures and the destruction of

the medieval London Bridge saw an end to the freezing of the Thames and frost fairs.

Mark the word outside the brackets that has a similar meaning to the words in both sets of brackets.

Example: (twig   branch)   (fasten   attach)   glue <u>stick</u> affix bough

13. (assist back up)   (prop crutch)   support brace encourage post

14. (trend style)   (build create)   construct mould fashion craze

15. (character symbol)   (message note)   post sign dispatch letter

16. (leap jump)   (tied secured)   vault truss bound hitched

17. (dressing bandage)   (smear spread)   daub plaster sticker gauze

Three of the words in each list are linked. Mark the word that is not related to these three.

Example: journal   diary   <u>textbook</u>   notebook

18. sour   bitter   sweet   tasteful

19. gruesome   horrific   volatile   awful

20. dragon   werewolf   antelope   phoenix

21. index   paperback   contents   glossary

22. north   left   forward   sideways

Find the word that means the same, or nearly the same, as the word on the left.

Example: **wide**   flat   straight   <u>broad</u>   long

23. **wall**   construct   remnant   enclosure   barricade

24. **infect**   tarnish   contaminate   infirm   puncture

25. **critical**   acute   utmost   intrinsic   fundamental

26. **traffic**   commotion   automobile   queue   congestion

END OF TEST

/ 26

Time for a break! This puzzle is a great way to practise your **vocabulary** skills.

Synonym Bridges

Continue the line to create a path from Adventurous Ernie along the word bridges to reach the blue flag. He has to cross the bridge that contains a word that's a synonym of the word on the last bridge he crossed. He can only cross each bridge once.

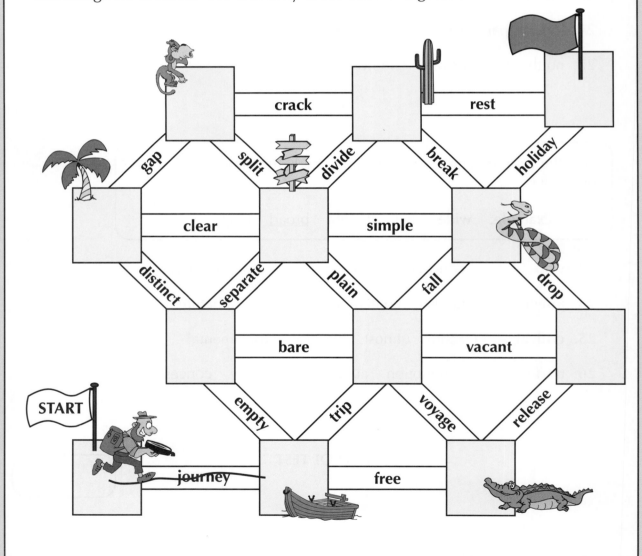

You have **10 minutes** to do this test. Work as quickly and as accurately as you can.

Fill in the missing letters to complete the words in the following passage.

1. In a world where hundreds of different `l` `_` `_` `g` `u` `_` `_` `e` `s` are

    spoken, it can be difficult for people from different countries to

2. `c` `_` `m` `m` `_` `_` `i` `c` `_` `t` `e`. Many people learn English as a

3. `s` `_` `_` `o` `_` `d` language, but many more don't. This means language

4. remains a common `b` `_` `_` `r` `_` `e` `_` between different people.

5. A Polish doctor called Ludwik Zamenhof identified this `_` `r` `o` `_` `_` `e` `m`

    and invented an international language called Esperanto. Words in Esperanto

6. are often `i` `_` `s` `p` `_` `_` `e` `d` by words from other languages, but made

7. less `c` `_` `m` `_` `_` `e` `_`. This makes it easier to learn — some say that

8. learning Esperanto takes a `q` `u` `_` `_` `_` `e` `_` of the time it takes to learn

9. other `f` `_` `r` `_` `_` `g` `_` languages.

10. Since its `c` `_` `e` `_` `_` `i` `_` `n`, millions of people have learned Esperanto,

11. including J.R.R. Tolkein, the `a` `_` `_` `t` `_` `_` `_` `r` of "The Lord of the Rings".

    Esperanto is still spoken by many people all over the world today,

12. making it the most `_` `u` `c` `_` `e` `s` `_` `_` `u` `l` invented language.

Three of the words in each list are linked. Mark the word that is not related to these three.

Example: journal   diary   <u>textbook</u>   notebook

13. autumnal   winter   summer   spring

14. loaf   baguette   brioche   roll

15. develop   adapt   persist   mutate

16. yen   coin   euro   dollar

17. lighthouse   pyramid   canyon   mausoleum

Mark the word outside the brackets that has a similar meaning to the words in both sets of brackets.

Example: (twig   branch)   (fasten   attach)   glue   <u>stick</u>   affix   bough

18. (learn   revise)   (office   library)   research   studio   work   study

19. (technique   knack)   (prank   joke)   skill   stunt   trick   jape

20. (sleet   precipitation)   (greet   salute)   address   rain   hail   welcome

21. (abandon   discard)   (fragment   piece)   scrap   shred   renounce   remnant

22. (forgive   pardon)   (pretext   alibi)   spare   excuse   reason   defence

Complete the word on the right so that it means the opposite, or nearly the opposite, of the word on the left.

Example: heavy [l][i][g][h][t]

23. driver   [ ][a][ ][s][e][ ][g][ ][r]

24. elegant   [g][ ][ ][c][e][ ][e][ ][s]

25. waste   [c][ ][n][ ][ ][r][ ][e]

26. unlimited   [f][ ][n][ ][t][ ]

END OF TEST

/ 26

You have **10 minutes** to do this test. Work as quickly and as accurately as you can.

Read this poem carefully and answer the questions that follow.

The Further Bank

I long to go over there to the further bank of the river,

    Where those boats are tied to the bamboo poles in a line;

    Where men cross over in their boats in the morning with ploughs

on their shoulders to till their far-away fields;

5   Where the cowherds* make their lowing cattle swim across to the riverside pasture;

    Whence they all come back home in the evening, leaving the

jackals to howl in the island overgrown with weeds,

    Mother, if you don't mind, I should like to become the boatman of the ferry when I am grown up.

    They say there are strange pools hidden behind that high bank,

10   Where flocks of wild ducks come when the rains are over, and thick

reeds grow round the margins where waterbirds lay their eggs;

    Where snipes** with their dancing tails stamp their tiny footprints upon the clean soft mud;

    Where in the evening the tall grasses crested with white flowers

invite the moonbeam to float upon their waves.

15   Mother, if you don't mind, I should like to become the boatman of the ferryboat when I am grown up.

    I shall cross and cross back from bank to bank, and all the boys and

girls of the village will wonder at me while they are bathing.

    When the sun climbs the mid sky and morning wears on to noon, I

shall come running to you, saying, "Mother, I am hungry!"

20   When the day is done and the shadows cower under the trees, I shall come back in the dusk.

    I shall never go away from you into the town to work like father.

    Mother, if you don't mind, I should like to become the boatman of the ferryboat when I am grown up.

Rabindranath Tagore

* cowherds — *cattle farmers*
**snipe — *a type of bird that lives in marshland*

Answer these questions about the text that you've just read.
Circle the letter that matches the correct answer.

1. Which of the following can not be found on the far river bank?

   A   Boats tethered to poles

   B   Land for grazing cattle

   C   Farmland

   D   Barns to store ploughing equipment

2. According to the text, what can be heard on the far side of the river bank at night?

   A   The sound of cows lowing

   B   The sound of jackals howling

   C   The call of wild ducks

   D   The sound of snipes stamping in the mud

3. "They say there are strange pools hidden behind that high bank" (line 9).
   What does this line tell us?

   A   The bank is too tall to climb over.

   B   The narrator has heard about the pools but not seen them.

   C   The wildlife enjoy living on the other side of the high bank.

   D   The pools are not visible because they are peculiar.

4. "in the evening the tall grasses crested with white flowers
   invite the moonbeam to float upon their waves" (lines 13-14).
   What does this mean?

   A   White flowers are only visible in the moonlight.

   B   During the night, the moonlight reflects off the grasses and flowers.

   C   The flowers and grasses are flooded in the evening.

   D   The moonlight is particularly attracted to the tall grasses.

5. "What does the word "cower" (line 20) mean?

  A   Crouch

  B   Envelop

  C   Lurk

  D   Sprawl

6. Which of the following are reasons why the narrator
   wants to become the boatman of the ferry?

  1.   The narrator wants to see what is on the other side of the river.
  2.   The narrator wants to help the cowherds and ploughmen.
  3.   The narrator wants to avoid bathing with the other children.
  4.   The narrator wants to stay with his mother.

  A   1 and 4

  B   3 and 4

  C   1, 2 and 4

  D   1, 3 and 4

7. Which of the following would not be used to describe the further bank?

  A   Cultivated

  B   Ethereal

  C   Immaculate

  D   Lively

Three of the words in each list are linked. Mark the word that is not related to these three.

  Example: journal   diary   <u>textbook</u>   notebook

---

8.   illness   unsanitary   sickness   disease

9. plate   fork   spoon   chopsticks

10. prodigy   elder   senior   guru

11. Mars   Venus   Moon   Saturn

12. mammal   animal   reptile   amphibian

13. react   initiate   acknowledge   counter

14. ravenous   peckish   replete   famished

Mark the word outside the brackets that has a similar meaning to the words in both sets of brackets.

Example: (twig   branch)   (fasten   attach)   glue <u>stick</u> affix bough

15. (narrative story)   (plan arrange)   scheme conspiracy tale plot

16. (quilt eiderdown)   (total inclusive)   duvet blanket general umbrella

17. (test experiment)   (lawsuit case)   assessment hearing trial research

18. (invoice statement)   (beak muzzle)   cheque score bill fare

19. (beat strike)   (ounce gram)   thump stone pound tonne

20. (usual ordinary)   (communal shared)   public routine typical common

END OF TEST

/ 20

(10)

You have **10 minutes** to do this test. Work as quickly and as accurately as you can.

Fill in the missing letters to complete the words in the following passage.

1. Individually, ants may seem fairly [p][ ][w][e][ ][ ][ ][s][s]. But, as a

2. group, they can [ ][ ][h][ ][e][v][ ] a wide range of tasks. For example,

3. finding and retrieving food is a job that can often [i][n][ ][ ][l][v][ ]

    thousands of ants.

4. The [s][ ][ ][r][ ][h] for food begins with the 'scout' ants, which leave the

5. ant colony. When one of them finds food, it takes a [p][ ][ ][c][ ] of it back

6. to the colony, and leaves a trail of [s][c][ ][n][ ][e][d] chemicals called

    pheromones, which it secretes from a gland in its body. The other ants can

7. smell these chemicals, so can [ ][o][l][ ][o][ ] the trail to the food.

    These ants then leave more pheromones, so the trail's smell becomes

8. [s][ ][ ][o][ ][ ][e][r], meaning more ants will take that trail and find

9. the food. Before long, a whole [ ][e][ ][w][o][r][ ] of paths is built up,

10. stretching out from the colony to a [v][ ][r][i][e][ ][ ] of food sources.

11. These trails can be used [r][ ][ ][e][a][t][e][ ][ ][y] in order to ensure

12. there is an [ ][d][e][ ][ ][a][t][ ] supply of food for the colony.

In each question below, the words can be rearranged to form a sentence. One word doesn't fit in the sentence. Underline the word that doesn't fit.

Example: red   the   has   <u>ride</u>   girl   bicycle   a

13. month   downpours   the   April   shower   there   throughout   of   were

14. carry   onto   bag   of   train   all   I   luggage   can   the   your

15. starts   cheer   the   playing   stage   normally   band   crowds   when

16. car   ask   way   to   stopped   for   the   directions   a   he   pedestrian

17. eventually   grow   your   lovable   will   dogs   naughty   become   puppies

Complete the word on the right so that it means the same, or nearly the same, as the word on the left.

Example: scared   (a)(f)(r)(a)(i)(d)

18. mistake   (b)(l)( )(n)( )( )(r)

19. quit   (r)( )(s)( )( )(n)

20. fate   (d)( )(s)( )( )(n)( )

21. naive   ( )( )(n)(o)( )( )(n)(t)

22. mystery   (e)( )( )(g)( )(a)

Find the word that means the opposite, or nearly the opposite, of the word on the left.

Example: **first**   later   <u>last</u>   next   beginning

23. **defy**   disregard   enact   conform   accost

24. **escape**   abscond   control   incarcerate   halt

25. **immune**   susceptible   emotional   gullible   docile

26. **friend**   confidant   nemesis   exponent   contender

END OF TEST

/ 26

You have **10 minutes** to do this test. Work as quickly and as accurately as you can.

Read this passage carefully and answer the questions that follow.

Vienna Philharmonic Orchestra

The Vienna Philharmonic Orchestra has won a wealth of accolades, including a Classical Brit Award in 2004 and three Grammy Hall of Fame Awards. Highlights in the Orchestra's calendar include a sell-out annual New Year Concert, in the fine concert hall in the Orchestra's home venue, and performances at the music festival in Salzburg. Events such as
5   these help the Orchestra keep its reputation as one of the best in the world.

Despite being the home of many musical greats, such as Haydn and Mozart, Vienna had no resident orchestra during the 18th century. Composers instead employed the orchestras of local opera groups to perform their works. For example, after moving from his hometown in Germany to Vienna, Beethoven debuted his ninth symphony with the combined forces of
10   several Viennese orchestras.

The predecessor of the Vienna Philharmonic, the Künstler-Verein (which translates as simply, 'Artists' Club'), was founded by Lachner, a German composer and conductor, in 1833. This group performed four concerts but then, for organisational reasons, disbanded. Nine years later however, Otto Nicolai revived Lachner's vision for a resident Viennese
15   orchestra, and established the 'Philharmonic Academy', now called the Vienna Philharmonic Orchestra. He stayed with the orchestra for five years, leading them in eleven concerts.

Arguably the most influential figure in the history of the Orchestra is Hans Richter, a conductor born in Hungary in 1843. Richter, who started working with the group at the age of 32, conducted the Orchestra in over 243 concerts, leading it to gain a world-class status.
20   Richter had to retire from conducting in 1911, but he is remembered for his incredible musical career, with his 23-year period with the Vienna Philharmonic Orchestra often being referred to as the 'Golden Era' in the Orchestra's history.

Today, the Orchestra has over 100 musicians and performs most frequently from its home at the Musikverein, situated opposite the popular Ressel Park in the Old Town of Vienna. In
25   the Great Hall, the magnificent concert hall within the venue that can seat over 1700 people, ticket holders can enjoy some of the best classical music concerts in the world.

Answer these questions about the text that you've just read.
Circle the letter that matches the correct answer.

1. When was the Vienna Philharmonic Orchestra founded?

   A   During the 17th century

   B   1833

   C   1842

   D   1855

2. According to the text, which statement applies to the Vienna Philharmonic Orchestra?

   A   It was the first orchestra based in Vienna.

   B   Lachner provided early inspiration for the Orchestra.

   C   It has always been conducted by an Austrian conductor.

   D   It was the first orchestra to perform Beethoven's ninth symphony.

3. When was the 'Golden Era' of the Vienna Philharmonic Orchestra?

   A   1843-1911

   B   1843-1866

   C   1875-1898

   D   1875-1911

4. According to the text, which of the following is false?

   A   The Vienna Philharmonic Orchestra is a multi-award-winning orchestra.

   B   The Vienna Philharmonic Orchestra only perform in the Musikverein.

   C   Otto Nicolai was involved in founding the Vienna Philharmonic Orchestra.

   D   The Vienna Philharmonic Orchestra was initially called the 'Philharmonic Academy'.

5. Which of the following is not mentioned in the text?
    A   The names of famous Austrian composers from the 1800s.
    B   The German translation of 'Artists' Club'.
    C   The capacity of the main concert hall in the Musikverein.
    D   How the size of the Vienna Philharmonic Orchestra has changed throughout history.

6. What do Beethoven and Richter have in common?
    A   They both moved to Vienna from elsewhere.
    B   They are both primarily remembered for their work as conductors.
    C   They were both members of the 'Artists' Club'.
    D   They both worked with the Philharmonic Academy.

7. According to the text, which of the following must be true?
    A   The Ressel Park adjoins Vienna Old Town.
    B   The New Year Concert is the largest event that the orchestra performs.
    C   Music by Beethoven is always performed at the annual Salzburg Music Festival.
    D   Over 1700 people attend the Vienna Philharmonic Orchestra's New Year Concert.

Mark the word outside the brackets that has a similar meaning to the words in both sets of brackets.

Example: (twig   branch)   (fasten   attach)   glue <u>stick</u> affix bough

8. (soul   mind)   (ghost   phantom)   spirit   spectre   personality   mood

9. (yearn   long)   (wood   fir)   crave   conifer   pine   wish

10. (silhouette form)   (statistic quantity)   sum figure physique frame

11. (lead command)   (chief boss)   order principal guide head

12. (praise acclaim)   (ascribe attribute)   credit assign applause kudos

13. (fear anxiety)   (siren horn)   signal shock panic alarm

14. (idol celebrity)   (planet asteroid)   satellite star luminary hero

---

Complete the word on the right so that it means the opposite, or nearly the opposite, of the word on the left.

Example: heavy   [l][i][g][h][t]

15. greeting   [f][a][ ][e][ ][ ][ ][l][l]

16. nervous   [ ][e][ ][a][x][ ][d]

17. tiny   [g][ ][ ][a][n][ ][ ][c]

18. believe   [ ][o][ ][b][ ]

19. expand   [c][ ][n][t][ ][ ][c][t]

20. defeat   [ ][i][ ][t][o][ ][ ]

END OF TEST

/ 20

You have **10 minutes** to do this test. Work as quickly and as accurately as you can.

Choose the correct words to complete the passage below.

Beatrix Potter is one of the world's best-selling and most

1. ☐ betrothed
    ☐ favourite children's
    ☐ greatest
    ☐ beloved

2. ☐ Renowned
    ☐ Obscure
    ☐ Enthusiastic
    ☐ Resented

authors.   for her popular animal characters, Potter wrote and

3. ☐ composed
    ☐ illustrated
    ☐ recorded   over 20 books.
    ☐ pictured

During her childhood, Potter

4. ☐ interested
    ☐ developed
    ☐ suffered   a passion for both animals and drawing.
    ☐ endorsed

While this

5. ☐ frequently
    ☐ initially
    ☐ never
    ☐ eternally

led her down a scientific career

6. ☐ business
    ☐ river
    ☐ choice   , she
    ☐ path

gradually began to focus more on illustrating. When on holiday and whilst working as

an illustrator, Potter wrote short stories which she

7. ☐ recorded
    ☐ posted
    ☐ dictated   to her friends' children
    ☐ recited

8. ☐ observed
   ☐ talented
   ☐ celebrated   character,
   ☐ memorialised

in letters. It was in these stories that she created her most

9. ☐ inclination
    ☐ satisfaction
    ☐ deliberation   to write books and, after facing
    ☐ limitation

Peter Rabbit. The letters gave Potter the

10. ☐ adoption
    ☐ harmony
    ☐ termination   from many publishers, Potter self-published
    ☐ rejection

11. ☐ their
    ☐ she
    ☐ her   first book in
    ☐ every

12. ☐ prompt
    ☐ immediate
    ☐ abject   success.
    ☐ veritable

1901. It was later printed by a publisher where it was an

Complete the word on the right so that it means the same, or nearly the same, as the word on the left.

Example: scared | a | f | r | a | i | d |

13. origin | s | | | r | | e |

14. fame | | e | | e | b | | i | | y |

15. haste | | r | g | | n | | y |

16. vary | f | | u | | t | u | | t | |

17. surround | | n | | i | | | l | e |

Three of the words in each list are linked. Mark the word that is not related to these three.

Example: journal   diary   <u>textbook</u>   notebook

18. multiply   equals   add   subtract

19. repair   demolish   mend   restore

20. burrow   warren   viaduct   tunnel

21. draughts   backgammon   solitaire   chess

Mark the word outside the brackets that has a similar meaning to the words in both sets of brackets.

Example: (twig   branch)   (fasten   attach)   glue   <u>stick</u>   affix   bough

22. (sketch design)   (stalemate tie)   heat   draw   outline   deadlock

23. (gamble chance)   (danger threat)   peril   wager   risk   fear

24. (obstruct seal)   (brick cube)   slab   barricade   plug   block

25. (period session)   (move relocate)   shift   carry   stint   transfer

26. (force attraction)   (importance seriousness)   value   pull   severity   gravity

END OF TEST

/ 26

Time for a break! These puzzles are a great way to practise your **word making** skills.

Anagram Sentences

Rearrange each of the words in brackets to make a
new word which completes the sentence.

1. Nobody wanted to speak to the (**nameless**) _____ at the door.

2. Jamie lives on a (**meteor**) _____ island.

3. Sally was the (**insect**) _____ person she'd ever met.

4. I walked into the (**thicken**) _____ and turned the kettle on.

5. The room was completely (**listen**) _____
    — there was no noise at all.

Words Within Words

Remove between one and four letters from each of the following
words to leave a word that has a similar meaning to the original word.

~~chicken~~   barren   charisma

           feast   separate

hen   _____   _____

           _____   _____

You have **10 minutes** to do this test. Work as quickly and as accurately as you can.

Fill in the missing letters to complete the words in the following passage.

1. In the [m][ ][t][ ][o][ ][o][g][y] of Ancient Greece, Orion was a strong but

2. arrogant hunter. There are different [s][t][ ][ ][i][e][ ] about Orion, and

3. though the details of some stories [c][o][ ][ ][r][a][ ][i][ ][t] each other,

4. there are common themes. One tale states that Orion [b][ ][a][ ][t][e][d]

    to Artemis, the goddess of the hunt, that he could kill any animal. This upset

5. Gaea, the goddess of nature, who sent a giant scorpion to [d][ ][f][ ][ ][t]

6. Orion. After a struggle, the scorpion was [ ][i][ ][ ][o][r][ ][o][u][s],

    and Orion was sent to the sky.

7. Today, Orion is best known for the constellation that [b][ ][a][ ][s] his name.

8. The constellation includes two of the [ ][ ][i][g][h][ ][ ][s][t] stars in the

9. night sky, as well as a [p][r][ ][m][ ][ ][e][n][t] group of stars known as

    "Orion's Belt". Another constellation is Scorpius — the scorpion that beat Orion

10. in the [l][e][ ][ ][n][ ]. Thankfully for Orion, Scorpius can only be seen

11. in the night sky [ ][u][ ][ ][n][g] summer, while Orion only

12. [a][p][ ][ ][ ][r][s] in the night sky throughout the winter months.

Three of the words in each list are linked. Mark the word that is not related to these three.

Example: journal diary <u>textbook</u> notebook

13. holiday anniversary commemoration jubilee

14. mast rudder yacht sail

15. alight dismount board disembark

16. name title christen dub

17. imposter charlatan felon fraud

Find the word that means the same, or nearly the same, as the word on the left.

Example: **wide** flat straight <u>broad</u> long

18. **candidate** option applicant employee newcomer

19. **stray** veer ramble deviate undulate

20. **calm** humour oblige pacify restrain

21. **fragrant** noxious pungent odour aromatic

22. **surrender** yield abate grovel subside

Mark the word outside the brackets that has a similar meaning to the words in both sets of brackets.

Example: (twig   branch)   (fasten   attach)   glue <u>stick</u> affix bough

23. (bat club)   (noise uproar)   din clamour paddle racket

24. (ingenuity skill)   (strategy proposal)   vision scheme initiative action

25. (prison dungeon)   (unit faction)   cell chamber section clique

26. (courteous polite) (internal domestic)   private civil decent affable

END OF TEST

/ 26

Test 17

You have **10 minutes** to do this test. Work as quickly and as accurately as you can.

Read this passage carefully and answer the questions that follow.

The RUBIK'S CUBE® 3D Puzzle

Since its invention in May 1974, the RUBIK'S CUBE® 3D puzzle has entertained and infuriated people the world over. It is believed that the six-faced puzzle can be arranged in 43 quintillion different ways, which makes it extremely tricky to solve. In fact, when he first invented it, Erno Rubik couldn't even solve his own puzzle.

5　A 29-year-old architecture professor in Budapest, Rubik created the first cube for his academic work. But after he had scrambled the cube, it took Rubik over a month to solve it. Once he realised its potential, Rubik manufactured his cube, and sold it in toy shops in Hungary as the "Magic Cube" (it was renamed for international release). From there, Rubik's invention was taken to the 1979 Nuremberg Toy

10　Fair, where it caught the eye of toy specialist Tom Kremer. Kremer was taken by the puzzle and worked with a United States-based company to sell it worldwide. However, the company didn't like the name "Magic-Cube" as they thought it implied it had links to witchcraft.

The *Rubik's Cube* 3D puzzle launched worldwide a mere six years after its

15　conception, and over 350 million have been sold globally since. It's believed that one in every seven people worldwide have attempted to solve the puzzle.

Rubik's invention has also spawned a new sport: speedcubing. Speedcubers try to solve a *Rubik's Cube* 3D puzzle in as fast a time as possible. The first International Championships were held in 1982. Puzzlers from around the world continue to

20　gather at the biennial competitions to put their skills to the test — the maximum number of required moves is 20, but the best can do it in fewer. The record holder is currently Mats Valk, from the Netherlands, with a time of 4.74 seconds, but he has yet to beat the robot Cubestormer III, which solved the puzzle in 3.25 seconds.

Answer these questions about the text that you've just read. Circle the letter that matches the correct answer.

1. Which of the following could be Erno Rubik's date of birth?

   A   21st March 1944

   B   13th July 1944

   C   17th August 1945

   D   11th December 1945

2. Where was Erno Rubik working in May 1974?

   A   At a toy shop in Hungary.

   B   At a toy fair in Nuremberg.

   C   At a university in Budapest.

   D   At an architects in the United States.

3. Which of the following explains why the "Magic Cube" was renamed?

   A   Rubik suggested that his name should be used for international release.

   B   The company thought the name "Magic Cube" could harm sales.

   C   The manufacturers were worried the cube may be used to practise witchcraft.

   D   The name "Magic Cube" was misleading as the cube wasn't magical.

4. In what year was the *Rubik's Cube's* global launch?

   A   1980

   B   1988

   C   1985

   D   1978

5. According to the text, which of the following must be false?

   A   Cubestormer III was designed to solve the puzzle.

   B   Mats Valk has been a speedcuber for eleven years.

   C   Valk's record is over a second slower than Cuberstormer III's record.

   D   The International Championships are held every year.

6. According to the text, which of the following must be true?

   A   It is more difficult to scramble the cube than to solve it.

   B   Erno Rubik took 31 days to solve his puzzle.

   C   Over half of the world's population have not tried to solve the puzzle.

   D   Tom Kremer was an expert in building toys.

7. Which of the following is not mentioned in the text?

   A   Erno Rubik's profession.

   B   Who holds the world speedcubing record.

   C   How much money *Rubik's Cube* 3D puzzles have made.

   D   Where Kremer first spotted Rubik's puzzle.

Find the word that means the opposite, or nearly the opposite, of the word on the left.

     Example: **first**   later   <u>last</u>   next   beginning

---

8. **concentrate**   hallucinate   congregate   decentralise   dissipate

9. **standard**   analogous   variant   disproportionate   calibre

10. **construct**   raze   fabricate   convert   vandalise

11. **loyal**   abiding   tentative   fickle   unsafe

12. **improve**   dwindle   deteriorate   tyrannise   oppress

13. **absorb**   quench   stifle   excrete   ingest

> In each question below, the words can be rearranged to form a sentence. One word doesn't fit in the sentence. Underline the word that doesn't fit.
>
> **Example**:   red   the   has   <u>ride</u>   girl   bicycle   a

14. cook   film   while   finished   shall   the   we   has   once   dinner

15. absence   attendance   a   lack   becoming   his   concern   was   of

16. a   Spain   they   year   money   to   plan   spend   next   in   month

17. cinema   at   times   the   four   afternoon   past   every   local   half   closes

18. scary   the   began   into   pumpkins   carved   cut   we   faces   to

19. butter   a   nor   strawberry   she   combination   peanut   jam   of   prefers   and

20. to   appreciated   give   charity   are   donations   any   greatly   appeal   the

END OF TEST

/ 20

You have **10 minutes** to do this test. Work as quickly and as accurately as you can.

Choose the correct words to complete the passage below.

1. ☐ sparsely
    ☐ remote
    ☐ seclude
    ☐ convenient

The tiny group of islands known as St. Kilda is the most [1] part of the

2. ☐ Located
    ☐ Find
    ☐ Between
    ☐ Parked

British Isles. [2] far off the north-west coast of Scotland, the islands of St. Kilda

3. ☐ partially
    ☐ utterly
    ☐ incredibly
    ☐ completely

are almost [3] uninhabited. The islands also have remarkable scenery,

4. ☐ except for
    ☐ including
    ☐ feature
    ☐ only

[4] rock formations known as stacks, which rise out of the sea off the coast

5. ☐ antisocial
    ☐ ordinary
    ☐ isolated
    ☐ frugal

of many of the islands. Perhaps because of this unique and [5] location,

6. ☐ penguins
    ☐ fraternities
    ☐ community
    ☐ colonies

St. Kilda is home to some of the largest seabird [6] in Europe. Among the

7. ☐ reside
    ☐ invade
    ☐ frequent
    ☐ chase

birds that [7] on the islands are Atlantic puffins and Northern Gannets — the

64

8. ☐ sole
   ☐ last's
   ☐ latter's   community is one of the largest in the world.
   ☐ other's

9. ☐ Expectantly
   ☐ Unexpectedly , the
   ☐ Tediously
   ☐ Unsurprisingly

islands are of great interest to seabird researchers, who

10. ☐ ignore
    ☐ monitor
    ☐ experiment   the birds all year
    ☐ hound

round. This surveillance has

11. ☐ concealed
    ☐ positioned
    ☐ apprehended   some bad news — the population of one
    ☐ uncovered

seabird, the kittiwake, has

12. ☐ escalated
    ☐ rebounded
    ☐ depleted   in recent years.
    ☐ cruised

Three of the words in each list are linked. Mark the word that is not related to these three.

Example: journal   diary   <u>textbook</u>   notebook

13. lemon   daffodil   lime   canary

14. haunted   possessed   cursed   unsettled

15. cathedral   abbey   castle   monastery

16. intermittent   sporadic   volatile   fitful

17. face   hand   pendulum   second

In each question below, the words can be rearranged to form a sentence. One word doesn't fit in the sentence. Underline the word that doesn't fit.

Example: red   the   has   <u>ride</u>   girl   bicycle   a

18. neither   at   amazed   his   made   was   Tim   discovery   shocked   nor

19. told   she   exaggerate   had   spiralling   control   was   of   lie   out   the

20. a   choices   salad   of   over   opted   I   for   other   the

21. pollution   cars   to   day   reduce   helps   walking   every   work   air

Mark the word outside the brackets that has a similar meaning to the words in both sets of brackets.

Example: (twig   branch)   (fasten   attach)   glue   <u>stick</u>   affix   bough

22. (breakthrough leap)   (proceed approach)   near   discovery   advance   find

23. (mood quality)   (timbre sound)   voice   tone   pitch   atmosphere

24. (builder inventor)   (devise contrive)   fix   engineer   creator   scheme

25. (donation bursary)   (allow permit)   accord   award   subsidy   grant

26. (snobbish haughty)   (senior manager)   superior   snooty   prime   uppity

END OF TEST

/ 26

You have **10 minutes** to do this test. Work as quickly and as accurately as you can.

Read this passage carefully and answer the questions that follow.

An abridged extract from 'The Eagle Cliff'

The nearest approach we have yet made to the sensation of flying is that achieved by
rushing down a long, smooth, steep hill-road on a well-oiled and perfect ball-bearings bicycle!
Barret had the broad road pretty much to himself.
Soon he entered the crowded thoroughfares, and was compelled to curb* both steed and
5 spirit. Passing through one of the less-frequented streets in the neighbourhood of Finchley
Road, he ventured to give the rein to his willing charger**.
But here Fortune ceased to smile.
Barret, although kind, courteous, manly, sensitive, and reasonably careful, was not just
what he ought to have been. Although a hero, he was not perfect. He committed the
10 unpardonable sin of turning a street corner sharply! A thin little old lady crossed the road
at the same identical moment, slowly. They met! Who can describe that meeting? Not the
writer, for he did not see it; more's the pity! Very few people saw it, for it was a quiet corner.
The parties concerned cannot be said to have seen, though they felt it. Both went down. It
was awful, really, to see a feeble old lady struggling with an athlete and a bicycle!
15   Two little street boys, and a ragged girl appeared as if by magic. They always do!
"Oh! I say! Ain't he bin and squashed 'er?"
Such was the remark of one of the boys.
"Pancakes is plump to 'er," was the observation of the other.
The ragged girl said nothing, but looked unspeakable things.
20   Burning with shame, trembling with anxiety, covered with dust and considerably bruised,
Barret sprang up, left his fallen steed, and, raising the little old lady with great tenderness in
his arms, sat her on the pavement with her back against the railings, while he poured out
abject apologies and earnest inquiries.

*curb — *restrain*   **R.M. Ballantyne**

** charger — *a horse ridden by a knight or soldier (here referring to Barret's bicycle)*

Answer these questions about the text that you've just read. Circle the letter that matches the correct answer.

1. Why did Barret have to slow down when he entered the town?

   A   He was worn out from cycling very fast.

   B   The road surfaces were poor.

   C   He was worried he may fall off his bike.

   D   The streets were filled with people.

2. What reason does the writer give for not describing the collision?

   A   The writer was not there to witness the collision.

   B   The collision happened too quickly.

   C   The collision was too awful to describe.

   D   The details of the collision aren't relevant to the story.

3. How do we know the collision was Barret's fault?

   A   Fortune was not on Barret's side.

   B   Barret doesn't always do the right thing.

   C   Barret took the corner too suddenly on his bicycle.

   D   The woman was more frail than Barret.

4. What does the boy mean by, "Pancakes is plump to 'er" (line 18)?

   A   The woman looks like she has been squashed.

   B   The woman looks pale, like a pancake.

   C   Compared to pancakes, the woman looks plump.

   D   The woman thinks that pancakes are thick.

5. When referring to the appearance of the children at the scene of the collision, what does the author mean by, "They always do!" (line 15)?

    A   There is always someone on hand to help when an accident happens.

    B   Someone always sees when you've done something wrong.

    C   There are always people in the streets around Finchley Road.

    D   People always seem to appear out of nowhere.

6. How does the girl who saw the collision react?

    A   She shouts insults at Barret.

    B   She glares at Barret.

    C   She helps the old lady to her feet.

    D   She talks to the boys about what happened.

7. How do we know Barret is worried about the old woman?

    A   He helps her stand up once she's fallen.

    B   He receives a lot of bruises from the collision.

    C   He is shaken and embarrassed.

    D   He asks the old lady whether she is alright.

In each question below, the words can be rearranged to form a sentence. One word doesn't fit in the sentence. Underline the word that doesn't fit.

Example: red   the   has   <u>ride</u>   girl   bicycle   a

---

8. lasts   hour   for   the   will   approximately   performance   one

9. expected   to   nobody   pass   his   test   driving   him   didn't

10. accomplished   a   that   painter   was   I   think   Monet   talented

11. on   was   small   the   she   shoes   too   but   dress   it   tried

12. they   clapping   loudly   the   cheered   performance   during

13. in   house   has   my   view   room   best   the   our   mine

14. was   a   prowling   through   hiding   tall   grass   the   tiger

Find the word that means the opposite, or nearly the opposite, of the word on the left.

Example: **first**   later   <u>last</u>   next   beginning

15. **neat**	unbalanced diligent amiss disorganised
16. **dull**	slippery unintelligent luminous smooth
17. **prevent**	impede facilitate disagree remonstrate
18. **contradict**	concur dispute coincide counteract
19. **rear**	forepart genesis apex leader
20. **bore**	exalt agitate obsess fascinate

END OF TEST

/ 20

You have **10 minutes** to do this test. Work as quickly and as accurately as you can.

Fill in the missing letters to complete the words in the following passage.

1.   The "Internet of Things" is an idea that's been around for d ☐ c ☐ ☐ e s ,

2.   but is only now becoming a r ☐ ☐ ☐ l i ☐ ☐ . The basic concept is that

3.   everyday domestic ☐ p ☐ l i a ☐ ☐ e s like toasters, kettles and

     fridges will be able to use technology and the Internet to work more

4.   e ☐ f i ☐ ☐ e n ☐ l y . For example, using sensors, your fridge

     might be able to identify when it's empty and notify you that it needs to be

5.   ☐ e f ☐ l ☐ ☐ d , or your heating system may be able to sense

6.   when there is nobody in the house and switch ☐ t s ☐ ☐ f off.

7.   These ideas can also be e ☐ p l ☐ ☐ e d in cities, such as sensors in

8.   roads that tell your car when there is a h ☐ z ☐ ☐ ☐ ahead.

9.   The "Internet of Things" offers opportunities, but some r ☐ ☐ ☐ s too.

10. Like other devices that are ☐ o n ☐ ☐ c ☐ e d to the Internet,

11. household items could be attacked by criminals — people may be ☐ a ☐ y

     of their electrical gadgets getting hacked. For now, the technology is still in its

12. i ☐ f a n ☐ ☐ , so we shall have to wait and see what the future holds.

Test 20

Find the word that means the same, or nearly the same, as the word on the left.

Example: **wide**   flat   straight   <u>broad</u>   long

13. **summary**   profile   synopsis   abbreviate   simplification

14. **caretaker**   steward   controller   waiter   labourer

15. **occur**   lapse   transpire   encounter   loom

16. **heir**   predecessor   substitute   beneficiary   ancestor

17. **catapult**   soar   grapple   skirmish   propel

Mark the word outside the brackets that has a similar meaning to the words in both sets of brackets.

Example: (twig   branch)   (fasten   attach)   glue   <u>stick</u>   affix   bough

18. (batter   lash)   (meal   self-service)   pound   buffet   strike   smorgasbord

19. (duo   pair)   (combine   connect)   match   integrate   conjoin   couple

20. (attract   interest)   (plea   request)   fascinate   petition   appeal   tempt

21. (provide   equip)   (appendage   limb)   arm   stock   extremity   steel

Complete the word on the right so that it means the opposite, or nearly the opposite, of the word on the left.

Example: heavy ⬜l⬜ ⬜i⬜ ⬜g⬜ ⬜h⬜ ⬜t⬜

22. sell ⬜ ⬜u⬜ ⬜ ⬜c⬜ ⬜ ⬜ ⬜s⬜ ⬜e⬜

23. attentive ⬜n⬜ ⬜ ⬜g⬜ ⬜l⬜ ⬜ ⬜ ⬜e⬜ ⬜ ⬜t⬜

24. asset ⬜l⬜ ⬜i⬜ ⬜ ⬜b⬜ ⬜i⬜ ⬜ ⬜i⬜ ⬜t⬜ ⬜

25. voluntary ⬜ ⬜o⬜ ⬜m⬜ ⬜ ⬜ ⬜l⬜ ⬜s⬜ ⬜ ⬜r⬜ ⬜y⬜

26. dissent ⬜c⬜ ⬜ ⬜n⬜ ⬜s⬜ ⬜ ⬜ ⬜s⬜ ⬜ ⬜s⬜

END OF TEST

/ 26

73

Test 20

Time for a break! These puzzles are a great way to practise your **vocabulary** skills.

Criss-Cross Opposites

Fill in the grid with words that have the opposite meaning of the words listed below. The number next to each word is the number of letters each new word has. Rearrange the letters in the grey boxes to find an antonym of plain.

cooked (3 letters)
disorderly (4 letters)
real (4 letters)
dead (5 letters)
harmless (5 letters)
cheap (6 letters)
despise (6 letters)
~~**passive** (6 letters)~~
roundabout (6 letters)
~~**baffle** (7 letters)~~
master (7 letters)
stressed (7 letters)
subside (9 letters)
deliberate (10 letters)
unimportant (11 letters)

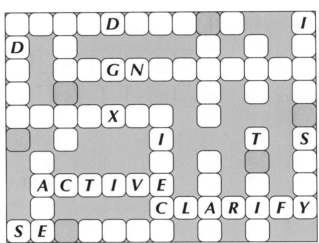

Antonym of plain:

_____

The Secret Word Vault

Use the letters in each box to make a word that is a synonym of the word 'secret'. You can use any letter in the box multiple times.

NIDHE

__ __ __ __ __ __

TFCIELDNOA

__ __ __ __ __ __ __ __ __ __

You have **10 minutes** to do this test. Work as quickly and as accurately as you can.

Read this passage carefully and answer the questions that follow.

Dick Turpin

There are hundreds of romantic stories about highwaymen — masked men who galloped across olden-day Britain on horseback, ambushing wealthy travellers. One such much-heroicised highwayman is Dick Turpin, whose true story is much more grisly than legend tells.

5   Born in 1705 into humble circumstances, Dick Turpin grew up in Essex. He is thought to have had little education and followed in the footsteps of his father to become a butcher.

After opening his own butcher's shop on the outskirts of London, Turpin started assisting a group of deer poachers active in the early 1730s known as the Essex

10   Gang. He was a useful contact for the gang, helping to dispose of the deer carcasses after a raid. Attracted by the money that could be gained as part of the group, Turpin eventually left his lowly life as a butcher and turned to a more full-time life of crime. In 1733, whilst running a pub, Turpin and other members of the Essex gang progressed from deer poaching to more extreme activities. They began raiding the

15   homes of farmers and landowners, often violently attacking anyone who tried to stop them.

As their robberies became increasingly high profile, the gang drew more attention from the authorities and a bounty was placed on the heads of the members. This caused the gang to disband as some members were caught and arrested, and others

20   fled to evade capture. It was around this time, in 1735, that Turpin turned to the occupation he is most noted for — highway robbery. As a highwayman, his violent attacks caused him to become known as 'Turpin the Butcher'.

Turpin's notorious career as a highwayman lasted for a few years, but he couldn't avoid the law forever. In October 1738, he was captured in Yorkshire after an

25   altercation in which he threatened to shoot a landlord. He was imprisoned in York Castle, where he was tried and found guilty. Six months later, he was hanged.

Answer these questions about the text that you've just read.
Circle the letter that matches the correct answer.

1. How are the stories told about highwaymen different to reality?

   A   Stories told nowadays are love stories.

   B   Today's stories describe highwaymen as bad characters.

   C   Gory details are often omitted from stories about highwaymen.

   D   Highwaymen are described as criminals in modern stories.

2. What is the most likely reason why Dick Turpin set up his own butcher's shop?

   A   He didn't spend much time at school.

   B   He learnt how to be butcher through the family business.

   C   He received money from gangs to help him buy a shop.

   D   Butchers' shops were popular in suburban London.

3. Why did Dick Turpin originally join the Essex Gang?

   A   He was trained in deer poaching.

   B   He lacked the skills to make his shop successful.

   C   He faced financial ruin if he stayed in the butcher's trade.

   D   He could earn more money through the gang than at his shop.

4. Which of these isn't given as a reason why the Essex Gang separated?

   A   Some members preferred deer poaching to house robberies.

   B   The crimes were becoming increasingly conspicuous.

   C   A reward was issued for the capture of members.

   D   Some members were scared of being caught.

5. According to the text, why was Turpin referred to as "Turpin the Butcher" (line 22) as a highwayman?

    A   He worked part-time as a butcher.

    B   He was famous for his brutal attacks.

    C   He needed to be distinguished from other highwaymen named Turpin.

    D   He was most noted for running a butcher's shop.

6. Which word below best describes Dick Turpin's career?

    A   Infamous

    B   Luxuriant

    C   Honourable

    D   Illustrious

7. Approximately how old was Dick Turpin when he died?

    A   32 years old

    B   34 years old

    C   35 years old

    D   40 years old

In each question below, the words can be rearranged to form a sentence. One word doesn't fit in the sentence. Underline the word that doesn't fit.

    Example: red   the   has   <u>ride</u>   girl   bicycle   a

8. house   invited   my   me   birthday   friend   over   celebrate   to   her

9. baked   the   for   had   the   in   cake   oven   too   been   long   burn

10. the   before   was   proofread   check   book   it   published   was   thoroughly

11. corner   garage   the   high   tool   rubbish   of   the   was   piled   with

12. walk   night   brass   a   the   last   marched   through   band   streets

13. stayed   several   watch   to   up   the   my   friends   fireworks   for   of

Complete the word on the right so that it means the same, or nearly the same, as the word on the left.

Example: scared   [a][f][r][a][i][d]

14. union   [m][a][ ][r][ ][ ][g][e]

15. plan   [p][ ][o][p][ ][s][a][ ]

16. poison   [ ][e][n][ ][m]

17. loud   [d][e][ ][ ][e][n][ ][n][g]

18. inactive   [d][ ][ ][ ][a][n][t]

19. eternal   [ ][n][d][u][ ][i][n][ ]

20. desert   [ ][b][a][ ][d][ ][ ]

END OF TEST

/ 20

You have **10 minutes** to do this test. Work as quickly and as accurately as you can.

Fill in the missing letters to complete the words in the following passage.

1. Training to be an airline pilot is an ⬚x⬚p⬚⬚n⬚s⬚⬚v⬚e and

2. demanding ⬚p⬚⬚o⬚c⬚e⬚⬚⬚, but the rewards can be significant for

3. those who make it through the ⬚⬚a⬚r⬚⬚o⬚⬚s stages of training.

4. ⬚A⬚s⬚⬚⬚i⬚⬚⬚i⬚n⬚g pilots need superior co-ordination, leadership and

5. problem-solving skills. Qualifications in ⬚s⬚u⬚⬚⬚e⬚c⬚⬚s like maths

    and physics are useful, though not essential, while all pilots must prove that they

6. are medically fit to fly in order to join an approved flight ⬚⬚c⬚h⬚⬚⬚⬚l.

    Before taking control of a real plane, trainees practise in specially designed

7. machines that ⬚m⬚⬚⬚i⬚c the conditions of flight. These flight simulators

8. ⬚⬚n⬚a⬚⬚l⬚e pilots to familiarise themselves with cockpit

9. controls and learn to fly safely and ⬚s⬚m⬚⬚⬚h⬚l⬚y.

    Trainee pilots will eventually earn a special licence called a 'frozen' Airline

10. Transport Pilot Licence (ATPL) which ⬚a⬚⬚l⬚⬚w⬚s them to become a

11. co-pilot. Co-pilots fly alongside a ⬚⬚u⬚a⬚⬚i⬚f⬚⬚e⬚d captain to gain

    experience before earning their full licence. After this, co-pilots can advance

12. their career in the ⬚s⬚k⬚⬚⬚s by training to become captains themselves.

79

Mark the word outside the brackets that has a similar meaning to the words in both sets of brackets.

Example: (twig   branch)   (fasten   attach)   glue   <u>stick</u>   affix   bough

13. (confront   tackle)   (residence   locality)   approach   address   area   abode

14. (set   situate)   (rank   grade)   place   arrange   classify   standing

15. (sobbed   wailed)   (roared   exclaimed)   bellowed   wept   cried   mourned

16. (luck   chance)   (wealth   riches)   providence   fortune   assets   funds

17. (rectify   amend)   (unerring   faultless)   ameliorate   exact   edit   correct

In each question below, the words can be rearranged to form a sentence. One word doesn't fit in the sentence. Underline the word that doesn't fit.

Example: red   the   has   <u>ride</u>   girl   bicycle   a

18. single   bells   chimes   the   loudly   hour   every   clock   town

19. blame   up   sister   me   in   my   mess   tried   kitchen   the   for   our   to

20. dogs   of   saw   steal   he   a   sausages   out   some   packet

21. see   Ben   to   listen   city   an   went   the   concert   in   amazing

22. his   my   learns   mischievous   from   never   mistakes   doesn't   cat

Find the word that means the opposite, or nearly the opposite, of the word on the left.

Example: **first**   later   <u>last</u>   next   beginning

23. **basic**   elaborate   complication   advance   arduously

24. **watertight**   absorbent   loose   repellent   permeable

25. **foolish**   prudent   skilful   profoundly   jocular

26. **pointless**   functioning   consequential   efficient   conceivable

END OF TEST

/ 26

You have **10 minutes** to do this test. Work as quickly and as accurately as you can.

Read this passage carefully and answer the questions that follow.

Glaciers

Glaciers are masses of ice that form when layers of unmelted snow are compacted. During the last ice age, which began 110,000 years ago and endured until around 11,500 BC, glacial ice covered a third of the Earth. Today, glacial ice covers a tenth of the Earth's land surface and is mostly found in polar regions (areas around the Arctic
5 and Antarctic poles).

Since around 1850, glaciers around the globe have been decreasing in size due to rising global temperatures, though they remain a common feature of the world's colder regions. However, glaciers are not restricted to polar areas and can exist wherever there are cool summer temperatures and regular snowfalls. Africa's Mount Kilimanjaro
10 is capped with glacial ice despite being equatorial.

Glaciers have helped to forge some of the world's most spectacular landscapes, including England's Lake District. Valley glaciers inch down mountains under their own weight like a river of ice, sometimes gliding on a layer of meltwater, carving out large flat-bottomed valleys. Valley glaciers can undergo a period of rapid movement
15 called a surge. The Kutiah Glacier, located in Pakistan, surged 7.5 miles over three months in 1953, travelling at an average speed of 367 feet per day.

Tidewater glaciers are valley glaciers that stretch onto the sea and form an ice shelf over the water. Icebergs are created when chunks of ice break away from these shelves in a process called calving. One such iceberg, nicknamed B-15, was
20 183 miles long and 23 miles wide; several pieces of B-15 were spotted close to New Zealand in 2011, eleven years after it calved from Antarctica's Ross Ice Shelf.

Unconfined by the rocky obstacles that surround valley glaciers, continental glaciers form giant ice sheets that can cover whole continents. Antarctica has been partly covered by ice for over 40 million years; some of its colossal ice sheet is three
25 miles thick and the largest glacier in the world, the 250-mile-long Lambert Glacier, is located here. However, since about the 1950s, hundreds of Antarctic glaciers have retreated in response to climate change; glacial ice is gradually melting and icebergs are being calved at a high rate.

Answer these questions about the text that you've just read.
Circle the letter that matches the correct answer.

1. Which of the following are not necessary for the formation of glaciers?

    1.   Valleys
    2.   Cool summer temperatures
    3.   Regular snowfall
    4.   Meltwater

    A   1 and 3
    B   1 and 4
    C   2 and 3
    D   3 and 4

2. Which of the following is not located in a polar region?

    A   The Ross Ice Shelf
    B   The Lambert Glacier
    C   Antarctic Ice Sheet
    D   The Kutiah Glacier

3. According to the text, which of the following statements must be false?

    A   Some of Antarctica's glaciers have advanced since the 1950s.
    B   The Kutiah Glacier moves 367 feet every day.
    C   The Kutiah Glacier stopped surging in 1953.
    D   Britain was predominantly covered in ice during the last ice age.

4. According to the text, which of these cannot cause glaciers to decrease in size?

    A   Lack of glacial surges
    B   Rising global temperatures
    C   Increased rate of iceberg calving
    D   Climate change

5. Which of these statements about B-15 is not mentioned in the text?

    A   B-15 broke apart into smaller pieces.

    B   B-15 floated away from where it was calved.

    C   B-15 was monitored by scientists.

    D   Parts of B-15 were still intact ten years after it calved.

6. According to the text, which of these statements must be true?

    A   10% of the world's total surface area is covered by glaciers.

    B   Antarctica has been entirely covered by ice for 40 million years.

    C   There was once glacial ice in the British Isles.

    D   There are no glaciers in Asia.

7. According to the text, which of the following statements must be false?

    A   Antarctica has had continental glaciers since before the last ice age.

    B   Antarctica's ice sheet was first created during the last ice age.

    C   Antarctica has at least one tidewater glacier.

    D   Continental glaciers can grow to be miles thick.

In each question below, the words can be rearranged to form a sentence. One word doesn't fit in the sentence. Underline the word that doesn't fit.

    Example: red   the   has   <u>ride</u>   girl   bicycle   a

---

8. too   always   music   Hiran   loudly   far   his   listens   plays

9. with   football   packed   people   park   who   was   the   playing

10. to   us   little   kept   my   brother   away   wanted   run   from   trying

11. letterbox   next   the   waited   the   arrive   Nadia   by   for   to   post

12. practicality   she   mind   on   designed   in   the   with   car

13. engineering   Max   study   university   at   learnt   to   decided

14. boom   tremendous   erupted   volcano   an   the   enormous   with

---

Find the word that means the opposite, or nearly the opposite, of the word on the left.

Example: **first**   later   <u>last</u>   next   beginning

---

15. **specific**   imprecise   unclearly   random   roughly

16. **tamed**   monstrosity   wilderness   fiercely   feral

17. **openly**   cowardly   stealth   covertly   allusive

18. **undying**   deadly   mortal   alive   fatal

19. **mature**   minor   juvenile   amateur   guileless

20. **frank**   secret   mutinous   timid   evasive

END OF TEST

/ 20

You have **10 minutes** to do this test. Work as quickly and as accurately as you can.

Choose the correct words to complete the passage below.

Alaska, the USA's northernmost state, is home to a

1. ☐ interesting
   ☐ difference   variety of cultures
   ☐ rich
   ☐ assorted

2. ☐ or
   ☐ and   traditions that have been passed down by Alaskan natives. There
   ☐ of
   ☐ to

3. ☐ is
   ☐ are
   ☐ was
   ☐ has

eleven key indigenous

4. ☐ community
   ☐ tribe   in Alaska,
   ☐ person
   ☐ cultures

5. ☐ any
   ☐ two   with their own language,
   ☐ both
   ☐ each

which have been categorised into five main groups. One such group

6. ☐ includes
   ☐ portrays   the
   ☐ feature
   ☐ holds

Yupik of southwest Alaska. Traditionally, the Yupik

7. ☐ reliant
   ☐ needed   on hunting, fishing and
   ☐ relied
   ☐ rested

foraging to survive. Like many Alaska Natives, they mainly lived a

8. ☐ sedentary
   ☐ nomadic   lifestyle,
   ☐ mobility
   ☐ disturbing

following the movements of the animals they

9. ☐ catch
   ☐ eaten   . During the winter months, they
   ☐ hunted
   ☐ keep

10.
came
☐ apart
☐ over
☐ together
☐ through
in small communities and stayed in seasonal settlements. Today,

many Yupik live more settled lives in villages that are
11.
☐ building
☐ located
☐ situation
☐ settling
on the same sites

where their ancient
12.
☐ ancestors
☐ families
☐ descendants
☐ ancestry
used to reside in winter; many still make a living

by hunting and fishing, and Elders pass on the Yupik culture to the next generation.

Find the word that means the opposite, or nearly the opposite, of the word on the left.

Example: **first**   later   <u>last</u>   next   beginning

13. **guilty**   innocence   blameless   irresponsible   contrite

14. **vice**   loosen   righteous   virtue   nobility

15. **native**   alienate   outsider   immigration   strange

16. **continue**   ending   conclusion   closure   adjourn

17. **moderate**   unruly   uncontrollable   extreme   excess

In each question below, the words can be rearranged to form a sentence. One word doesn't fit in the sentence. Underline the word that doesn't fit.

Example: red   the   has   <u>ride</u>   girl   bicycle   a

18. Sunday   married   Elsa   morning   getting   cousin   is   my   tomorrow   on

19. puncture   the   bin   had   discarded   its   a   bike   in   tyre

20. rude   it   I   to   would   ignore   if   be   think   very   them

21. valley   are   search   nestled   the   find   those   that   castles   go   in   and

Three of the words in each list are linked. Mark the word that is not related to these three.

Example: journal   diary   <u>textbook</u>   notebook

22. action   adventure   dramatic   fantasy

23. tropical   mountainous   arctic   ocean

24. span   bypass   cross   traverse

25. towpath   lane   aisle   bridleway

26. acrobatic   agile   muscular   dexterous

END OF TEST

/ 26

You have **10 minutes** to do this test. Work as quickly and as accurately as you can.

> Read this passage carefully and answer the questions that follow.

An abridged extract from 'A Christmas Carol'

The Phantom slowly, gravely, silently, approached. When it came near him, Scrooge bent down upon his knee; for in the very air through which this Spirit moved it seemed to scatter gloom and mystery.

It was shrouded in a deep black garment, which concealed its head, its face, its
5   form, and left nothing of it visible save one outstretched hand.

"I am in the presence of the Ghost of Christmas Yet To Come?" said Scrooge.

The Spirit answered not, but pointed onward with its hand.

"You are about to show me shadows of the things that have not happened, but will happen in the time before us," Scrooge pursued. "Is that so, Spirit?"
10   The upper portion of the garment was contracted for an instant in its folds, as if the Spirit had inclined its head. That was the only answer he received.

Although well used to ghostly company by this time, Scrooge feared the silent shape so much that his legs trembled beneath him, and he found that he could hardly stand when he prepared to follow it. The Spirit paused a moment, as
15   observing his condition, and giving him time to recover.

But Scrooge was all the worse for this. It thrilled him with a vague uncertain horror, to know that behind the dusky shroud*, there were ghostly eyes intently fixed upon him, while he, though he stretched his own to the utmost, could see nothing but a spectral hand and one great heap of black.
20   "Ghost of the Future!" he exclaimed, "I fear you more than any spectre I have seen. But as I know your purpose is to do me good, and as I hope to live to be another man from what I was, I am prepared to bear you company, and do it with a thankful heart. Will you not speak to me?"

It gave him no reply. The hand was pointed straight before them.
25   "Lead on!" said Scrooge. "Lead on!"

Charles Dickens

* shroud — *a piece of cloth that is wrapped*
            around a body before it is buried

Answer these questions about the text that you've just read.
Circle the letter that matches the correct answer.

1. According to the text, which of the following must be true?

   A   Scrooge knew something about the Ghost before meeting him.

   B   Scrooge is immediately sure about the identity of the Ghost.

   C   Scrooge has met the Ghost before.

   D   Scrooge has no idea why the Ghost has appeared.

2. What does the word "inclined" (line 11) mean?

   A   Disposed

   B   Bowed

   C   Shook

   D   Slanted

3. Why was Scrooge filled with a "vague uncertain horror" (line 16-17)?

   A   He was struggling to see anything.

   B   He knew the Ghost was looking at him, but he couldn't see its eyes.

   C   The Ghost started to move towards him.

   D   He thought the Ghost meant to grab him.

4. Which of these words could not be used to describe the Ghost?

   A   Malicious

   B   Mute

   C   Veiled

   D   Perceptive

5. According to the text, which of the following is false?

   A   Scrooge is used to seeing ghosts.

   B   Scrooge has spent time with another ghost.

   C   Scrooge no longer fears ghosts.

   D   Scrooge has seen at least two ghosts.

6. Why does Scrooge decide to go with the Ghost?

   A   He thinks the Ghost will show him something exciting.

   B   He isn't afraid of the Ghost.

   C   He is afraid to disobey the Ghost.

   D   He believes the Ghost is there to help him.

7. Which of the following is true about Scrooge?

   A   He has no aspirations for the future.

   B   He isn't interested in seeing his future.

   C   He allows fear to get the better of him.

   D   He doesn't like the person that he has been in the past.

In each question below, the words can be rearranged to form a sentence.
One word doesn't fit in the sentence. Underline the word that doesn't fit.

Example: red   the   has   <u>ride</u>   girl   bicycle   a

---

8. wolf   eyes   mournfully   its   looking   the   piercing   with   stared

9. give   end   you   it's   away   not   story   fair   the   of   to   the

10. into   bus   there   town   travelling   are   routes   go   that   two

11. showing   the   favourite   be   at   cinema   film   is   again   my

---

12. back   accident   came   scooter   they   off   when   to   fell   she   help   her

13. went   an   of   gallery   paintings   many   had   I   art   lots   to   that

14. than   finished   cross-country   hour   in   she   less   race   over   the   an

---

Complete the word on the right so that it means the same, or nearly the same, as the word on the left.

Example: scared | a | f | r | a | i | d |

---

15. shortfall | d | e | | i | c | i | | n | c | |

16. purpose | o | b | | e | c | | i | | e |

17. flood | | e | l | u | | e |

18. keep | d | | | a | i | n |

19. thrifty | | c | o | | o | | i | c | | l |

20. expire | p | e | | i | | h |

END OF TEST

/ 20

Time for a break! This puzzle is a great way to practise your **vocabulary** skills.

Synonym Scroll

Caius is trying to solve a word puzzle to reveal the name of a famous Roman monument located in Britain. In the puzzle, each word crosses over at least one other word that has the same or nearly the same meaning as it.
Fill in the missing letters, then unscramble the letters in the blue boxes to reveal the name of the monument. Write it at the top of the scroll.

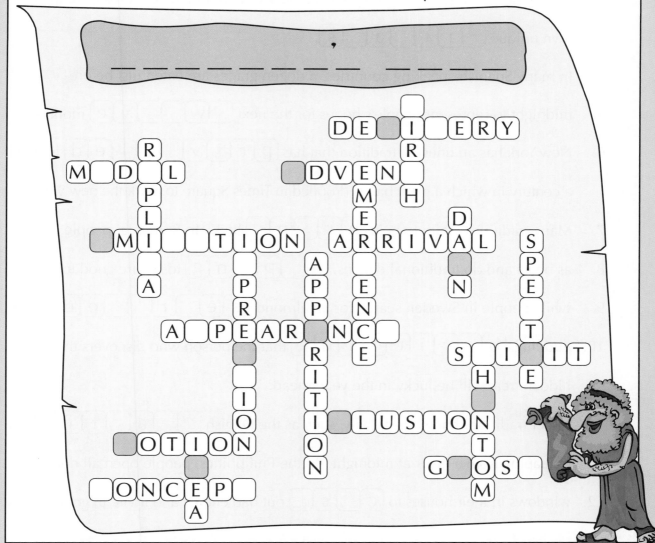

Test 26

You have **10 minutes** to do this test. Work as quickly and as accurately as you can.

Fill in the missing letters to complete the words in the following passage.

1. In many cultures, the ☐e☐g☐☐n☐☐i☐☐g of a new year is a

2. t☐☐e of great celebration. Firework displays are commonly used to

3. herald the ☐r☐☐i☐☐a☐l of a new year, but many cultures have their

4. own unique ☐i☐t☐☐a☐☐s.

   In many Spanish-speaking countries, a dozen grapes are eaten just before

5. midnight to represent people's hopes for the next ☐w☐☐☐v☐e months.

6. New York has an unusual tradition that has p☐r☐☐v☐☐☐l☐e☐d for over

   a century in which a giant ball is dropped in Times Square to mark the new year.

7. Many traditions claim to help b☐r☐☐n☐☐ luck. In Romania, people dress

8. as bears and do traditional dances, h☐☐p☐☐n☐g to secure good fortune,

9. while people in Sweden search for an almond, s☐e☐☐r☐☐☐e☐d in rice

10. pudding, b☐☐☐i☐e☐☐i☐n☐g that the person who discovers the

    hidden treat will be lucky in the year ahead.

11. Other traditions banish negativity, such as the Danish ☐r☐a☐☐t☐i☐☐e

    of leaping from a chair at midnight. In the Philippines, people open all doors and

12. windows in their houses to c☐☐s☐☐ out bad energy and invite in good energy.

     94

Find the word that means the same, or nearly the same, as the word on the left.

Example: **wide**   flat   straight   <u>broad</u>   long

13. **procedure**   commencement   operations   method   configuration

14. **meeting**   encounter   lecture   gather   confrontation

15. **support**   abet   conserve   extend   bolster

16. **happen**   occurrence   ascend   ensue   instigate

17. **respectful**   attentive   reverent   worshipping   saintly

Three of the words in each list are linked. Mark the word that is not related to these three.

Example: journal   diary   <u>textbook</u>   notebook

18. cleanse   purify   boil   fumigate

19. debit   divide   subtract   deduct

20. carpet   rug   floorboard   mat

21. coalition   collaboration   institute   alliance

22. vicar   disciple   priest   pastor

In each question below, the words can be rearranged to form a sentence. One word doesn't fit in the sentence. Underline the word that doesn't fit.

Example: red   the   has   <u>ride</u>   girl   bicycle   a

23. a   that   goalkeeper   saved   stop   shot   didn't   team's   single

24. can   very   learning   speak   new   rewarding   a   be   language

25. in   are   front   brother's   there   rabbits   cottage   of   near   my

26. actually   together   another   they   quite   one   were   to   similar

END OF TEST

/ 26

You have **10 minutes** to do this test. Work as quickly and as accurately as you can.

Read this passage carefully and answer the questions that follow.

The Floating City

The city of Venice, nestled in the north-eastern corner of Italy, has long been
regarded as one of Europe's most remarkable cities. It was founded around 400 AD
when refugees settled on an archipelago of islands in the Venetian Lagoon, a sheltered
bay of the Adriatic sea. Settlers began the construction of this great city which consists
5 of a myriad of stone buildings resting upon stilts, driven into the bed of the lagoon.
The buildings appear to float serenely on the surface of the lagoon, earning Venice the
epithet 'The Floating City'.

The city's prosperity saw it become the capital of the Republic of Venice, a burgeoning
maritime power that emerged in the late 7th century AD. Though the dismantling of the
10 Republic of Venice saw Venice lose much of its power, its influences on art, music and
literature meant that it remained a cultural centre. Today, just over 200 years since the
final days of the Republic of Venice, the city's diminishing population is reliant on tourism
for much of its income. A popular destination within the city is St Mark's Square. Here,
tourists can explore Venice's cathedral and the adjacent Doge's Palace, which stand on the
15 east side of the square, opposite Museum Corner. The north side of the square features a
Renaissance-style clock tower that faces towards the lagoon. Tourists must plan their visits
carefully, however. St Mark's Square and much of Venice, the 'City of Water', is prone to
flooding temporarily during particularly big tides. Locals call this phenomenon *acqua alta*.

Though cars are permitted in parts of modern Venice, the historic centre is free of
20 roads. Instead, over 170 man-made canals criss-cross the city, spanned by a collection
of more than 400 bridges. Many of the 55,000 residents of 'The City of Canals'
now use motorised boats, though Venice's waterways were traditionally navigated in
boats like the gondola, which gondoliers would skilfully propel forward using a long
pole. Today, gondolas are used almost exclusively by tourists, who often outnumber
25 Venetians on the busiest days of the season.

Answer these questions about the text that you've just read. Circle the letter that matches the correct answer.

1. Between which dates did the Republic of Venice exist?
    A   Around 400 AD – 1700 AD
    B   Around 600 AD – 1700 AD
    C   Around 600 AD – 1800 AD
    D   Around 700 AD – 1800 AD

2. Which of the following is not mentioned in the text?
    A   The proportion of Venetians who use motorised boats.
    B   The term used to describe those who operate a gondola.
    C   The name of the palatial residence found in St Mark's Square.
    D   The term Venetians give to describe tidal flooding.

3. Which of the following best describes the location of Venice?
    A   Adjacent to the Adriatic Sea, to the east of Italy.
    B   To the north-east of Italy.
    C   In an enclosed area of the Adriatic Sea, in north-east Italy.
    D   In a sheltered bay, situated in the north-east Adriatic Sea.

4. Which of these statements apply to buildings in old Venice?
    1.   Many are built on bridges.
    2.   They can only be reached by boat.
    3.   They are often built on stilts.
    4.   Some are at risk of flooding.

    A   1 and 4
    B   1, 3 and 4
    C   2 and 3
    D   3 and 4

5. Which of these statements is true?

    A   Doge's Palace is directly opposite the clock tower.

    B   The cathedral is opposite Doge's Palace.

    C   The facade of the cathedral faces towards the lagoon.

    D   Museum Corner is in the west of St. Mark's Square.

6. Which of these is not a name given to the historic city of Venice?

    A   The City of Water

    B   Europe's Most Remarkable City

    C   The Floating City

    D   The City of Canals

7. Which of these statements cannot be true?

    A   Great writers and composers have been inspired by Venice.

    B   There are more than 55,000 tourists in Venice on some days.

    C   There are more residents in Venice today than 500 years ago.

    D   The settlers who first formed Venice came from outside of Italy.

Complete the word on the right so that it means the opposite, or nearly the opposite, of the word on the left.

Example: heavy | l | i | g | h | t |

---

8. prove | r | e | | u | | e |

9. uncertain | r | | s | | | u | t | e |

10. detract | e | | | a | n | | e |

11. uplift | d | a | | p | | n |

Test 27

12. claim r e ☐ ☐ n q u ☐ ☐ h

13. inclusion o m ☐ ☐ ☐ i o n

14. start ☐ e r m i ☐ a ☐ e

Three of the words in each list are linked. Mark the word that is not related to these three.

Example: journal diary <u>textbook</u> notebook

---

15. seafarer submariner motorist yachtswoman

16. radio projector speaker headphones

17. ferment decay disperse curdle

18. roundabout carousel escalator turntable

19. tenacity endurance power persistence

20. incensed envious begrudging jealous

END OF TEST

/ 20

Test 28

You have **10 minutes** to do this test. Work as quickly and as accurately as you can.

Choose the correct words to complete the passage below.

Before the 20th century, many

1. ☐ hospitals
☐ physicians
☐ doctor
☐ nurse

and scientists thought that the brain shut

down during sleep. However, this belief was

2. ☐ disproved
☐ initiated
☐ mistaken
☐ unconfirmed

in the 20th century

after the EEG machine was

3. ☐ founded
☐ creation
☐ discovery
☐ invented

in 1924.

EEG machines measure brain activity by

4. ☐ monitoring
☐ realising
☐ spying
☐ creating

electrical signals produced by

the brain, also

5. ☐ called
☐ named
☐ seen
☐ known

as 'brain waves'.

6. ☐ Since
☐ Before
☐ By
☐ Afterwards

the 1920s, scientists

have used EEG machines to carry out many

7. ☐ importance
☐ groundbreaking
☐ numerate
☐ lots

sleep studies,

which have since revealed that there

8. ☐ is
☐ was
☐ are
☐ be

actually several distinct stages of sleep.

9.
One of these
- ☐ places
- ☐ phases
- ☐ type
- ☐ part

is called REM sleep, during which the brain is actually

10.
- ☐ verily
- ☐ much
- ☐ highly
- ☐ incredible

active; most dreams occur during this stage of sleep. Some scientists

11.
have
- ☐ opposed
- ☐ theorised
- ☐ preferred
- ☐ submitted

that dreams are a visual by-product of the brain sifting through the

12.
day's experiences and deciding
- ☐ what
- ☐ whose
- ☐ those
- ☐ them

information should be stored as memories.

Complete the word on the right so that it means the opposite,
or nearly the opposite, of the word on the left.

Example: heavy | l | i | g | h | t |

---

13. surplus | d | e | f | | c | | t |

14. thriving | s | t | | | g | | l | i | n | g |

15. untreatable | c | u | | | b | | e |

16. refined | c | | | d | e |

17. factual | f | | c | t | | t | i | | u | s |

Mark the word outside the brackets that has a similar meaning to the words in both sets of brackets.

Example: (twig   branch)   (fasten   attach)   glue <u>stick</u> affix bough

18. (soar   escalate)   (missile   projectile)   weapon   inflate   shoot   rocket

19. (tumult   turmoil)   (illness   affliction)   disorder   mayhem   malady   bedlam

20. (scour   search)   (untangle   groom)   sweep   disentangle   comb   rake

21. (regroup   reunite)   (meeting   assembly)   revival   rally   alliance   reassemble

22. (steam   iron)   (pulp   squash)   press   mash   flatten   pulverise

In each question below, the words can be rearranged to form a sentence. One word doesn't fit in the sentence. Underline the word that doesn't fit.

Example: red   the   has   <u>ride</u>   girl   bicycle   a

23. every   is   it   darker   has   evening   been   earlier   getting

24. cousin   it   home   my   me   took   hours   to   two   cycle

25. number   the   through   Nile   African   flows   Egypt   countries   a   River   of

26. an   scared   spotting   fear   the   elephant   cowered   man   in   after

END OF TEST

/ 26

Test 28

You have **10 minutes** to do this test. Work as quickly and as accurately as you can.

Read this poem carefully and answer the questions that follow.

The Story of Grumble Tone

There was a boy named Grumble Tone, who ran away to sea.
'I'm sick of things on land,' he said, 'as sick as I can be,
A life upon the bounding wave is just the life for me!'
But the seething ocean billows failed to stimulate his mirth,
5   For he did not like the vessel or the dizzy rolling berth,
And he thought the sea was almost as unpleasant as the earth.

He wandered into foreign lands, he saw each wondrous sight,
But nothing that he heard or saw seemed just exactly right,
And so he journeyed on and on, still seeking for delight.
10   He talked with kings and ladies grand; he dined in courts, they say,
But always found the people dull and longed to get away
To search for that mysterious land where he should want to stay.

He wandered over all the world, his hair grew white as snow,
He reached that final bourne* at last where all of us must go,
15   But never found the land he sought; the reason would you know?
The reason was that north or south, where'er his steps were bent,
On land or sea, in court or hall, he found but discontent,
For he took his disposition with him, everywhere he went.

Ella Wheeler Wilcox

*bourne — *boundary or destination*

          104

Answer these questions about the text that you've just read.
Circle the letter that matches the correct answer.

1. What does "seething ocean billows" (line 4) suggest?

   A   The sea is irate.

   B   The sea is making a loud racket.

   C   The conditions on the sea are rough.

   D   There is a breeze blowing over the sea.

2. Why did Grumble Tone come to dislike being on the sea?

   A   He was afraid of living on a boat.

   B   He didn't like the motion of the boat on the sea.

   C   His lodgings on the boat were too small.

   D   He'd seen everything there was to see on the sea.

3. What made Grumble Tone journey "on and on, still seeking for delight" (line 9)?

   A   He couldn't find anything to see in the foreign lands he visited.

   B   He was bored by the sights of foreign lands.

   C   There was always something lacking wherever he travelled.

   D   He wanted to travel towards a specific place.

4. Line 14 states that Grumble Tone "reached that final bourne at last where all of us must go". What does this tell us about Grumble Tone's fate?

   A   He eventually found somewhere that he wanted to stay.

   B   He decided to stop travelling.

   C   He was joined by others at his final destination.

   D   His final destination was death.

5. Which of these words best describes Grumble Tone's attitude throughout his travels?

    A   Distressed

    B   Anguished

    C   Disaffected

    D   Imperious

6. Why did Grumble Tone find "but discontent" (line 17) regardless of where he travelled?

    A   He had a poor outlook on life.

    B   Nobody would speak to him.

    C   He didn't actually want to travel.

    D   He only visited boring places.

7. What is the significance of Grumble Tone's name?

    A   It tells us which family he is from.

    B   It tells us his voice was low and gruff.

    C   It tells us he was liable to complaining.

    D   It tells us he enjoyed grumbling about the things he heard.

In each question below, the words can be rearranged to form a sentence. One word doesn't fit in the sentence. Underline the word that doesn't fit.

    Example: red   the   has   <u>ride</u>   girl   bicycle   a

---

8. cunning capture week evaded thieves occasion again the this

9. by been all were late sold books of February the

10. never quite anything before I'd like nothing seen it

11. opening he the crisps always crushes before there the packet

12. the stayed last after show performed for everyone tea night

13. are unclaimed there some property of items lots lost in

14. college October his away is sister to in going attending

Mark the word outside the brackets that has a similar meaning to the words in both sets of brackets.

Example: (twig   branch)   (fasten   attach)   glue <u>stick</u> affix bough

15. (match fight)   (stint spell)   struggle bout stretch heat

16. (advances progresses) (takings revenue)   proceeds earnings profits moves

17. (swing gravitate)   (cultivate nurture)   cherish drift sustain tend

18. (beacon signal)   (flicker flame)   flashlight smoulder flare glow

19. (undertaking mission) (business company)   pursuit affair enterprise franchise

20. (woo romance)   (arena stadium)   ground court flirt rink

END OF TEST

/ 20

You have **10 minutes** to do this test. Work as quickly and as accurately as you can.

Fill in the missing letters to complete the words in the following passage.

1. Ancient Egypt was a sophisticated s [ ] c i [ ] t y . As well as

2. b [ ] [ ] l d [ ] [ ] g many great structures, such as the pyramids, they had

3. a c [ ] m p [ ] [ ] x writing system. One Egyptian script is called

4. Hieroglyphic script, which was written down in r [ ] [ ] s or columns. This

5. script is made up of various [ ] [ ] m b [ ] l s , images and figures called

   hieroglyphs that represent certain sounds, syllables and words.

6. Used mainly by Ancient Egyptian priests for s [ ] c r [ ] d purposes,

7. hieroglyphs a [ ] o [ ] n many Egyptian temples and tombs. However, by

   the 4th century AD, Egypt had become more Christian and the use and

8. understanding of hieroglyphs had d e [ ] l [ ] n e [ ] .

   For over a millennia, nobody knew how to translate hieroglyphs, but this changed

9. after the discovery of the Rosetta Stone in 1799. This [ ] r [ ] e f a [ ] t

10. is inscribed with a royal decree [ ] r i [ ] t [ ] n in Egyptian hieroglyphs,

    Demotic (another Egyptian script) and, crucially, Greek. This stone was an

11. [ ] n v [ ] l u a [ ] l [ ] find as it enabled scholars to use knowledge

12. of Ancient Greek to d [ ] c [ ] p [ ] e r each hieroglyph's meaning.

Mark the word outside the brackets that has a similar meaning to the words in both sets of brackets.

Example: (twig   branch)   (fasten   attach)   glue <u>stick</u> affix bough

13. (welcome   accept)   (hug   cuddle)   receive clasp embrace adopt

14. (execute   achieve)   (register   discern)   actualise realise get attain

15. (skewer   rod)   (sizzle   sputter)   spit hiss spike crackle

16. (wave   brandish)   (grow   prosper)   wield flourish flower evolve

17. (jostle   manhandle)   (assume   carry)   accept nudge ram shoulder

Three of the words in each list are linked. Mark the word that is not related to these three.

Example: journal   diary   <u>textbook</u>   notebook

18. fudge   caramel   sugar   toffee

19. flighty   erratic   impulsive   eager

20. rosette   certificate   badge   ticket

21. avalanche   blizzard   snowdrift   typhoon

22. jumping   diving   sailing   swimming

Find the word that means the same, or nearly the same, as the word on the left.

Example: **wide**   flat   straight   <u>broad</u>   long

23. **weakened**   infirmary   ailment   debilitated   fragility

24. **avoid**   elude   circumference   intercept   deter

25. **animate**   activate   trigger   motivate   enliven

26. **allowed**   vowed   authorised   proclamation   declared

END OF TEST

/ 26

You have **10 minutes** to do this test. Work as quickly and as accurately as you can.

Read this passage carefully and answer the questions that follow.

The Boat Races

In the men's and women's Boat Races, boats of eight rowers from the universities
of Oxford and Cambridge compete over a gruelling course on the River Thames.
The first Boat Race was held in 1829 when Charles Wordsworth and Charles
Merivale, from Oxford University and Cambridge University respectively, organised a
5 race between their university boat clubs. The two old school friends competed
head-to-head and Wordsworth's crew claimed victory. This was the beginning of the
long-running tradition of the men's Boat Race. The first women's Boat Race was held
98 years later. Both races are now popular, competitive events.
Today, the Boat Race is 6.8 km long and takes place on the Tideway from Putney
10 to Mortlake. The race is rowed upstream with the incoming tide, allowing crews
to take advantage of the favourable current. Bad weather can make the Tideway a
rough stretch of water and boats have sunk in choppy conditions. It's the role of the
cox, who sits in the boat with the rowers, to steer a course through the difficult water.
One notable event in the race's history occurred in the 2012 men's race. A
15 swimmer entered the Thames at Chiswick Eyot, a narrow island around the half-way
mark, and swam towards the finish, moving into the path of the oncoming boats at
Chiswick Steps. The boats were stopped while the swimmer was arrested. The race
was restarted, but a collision between the racing boats quickly followed, in which
an Oxford rower's oar was broken. The umpire deemed the collision to be Oxford's
20 fault and the race was allowed to continue. With one man unable to row in the
Oxford boat, Cambridge raced to victory.
Developments in equipment and training have seen the Boat Races become faster
throughout the years. The first men's Boat Race on the current course was won in 1845
in a time of 23 minutes and 30 seconds, though the course record, set in 1998, is
25 16 minutes and 19 seconds. The record time for the women's race on the same course
is 19 minutes and 45 seconds.

Answer these questions about the text that you've just read.
Circle the letter that matches the correct answer.

1. In total, how many people take part in the men's Boat Race?

   A   8

   B   9

   C   16

   D   18

2. According to the text, what is the Tideway?

   A   The name of a river.

   B   A section of the River Thames.

   C   The type of boat that the crews row in.

   D   A rowing venue near Henley.

3. According to the passage, which of the following must be true?

   A   Charles Wordsworth and Charles Merivale went to the same university.

   B   Charles Wordsworth learned to row at school.

   C   The 1829 boat race was completed in under 24 minutes.

   D   Oxford won the first ever boat race.

4. In the course of the Boat Race, where is Chiswick Eyot?

   A   Closer to Putney than Mortlake

   B   Downstream from Mortlake

   C   Upstream from Chiswick Steps

   D   3.2 miles from Putney

5. According to the passage, which of the following must be false?

   A   The men's Boat Race has taken place more times than the women's.

   B   The course is shorter now than when the race was first held.

   C   Coxes are responsible for steering the racing boats.

   D   Year on year, the men's Boat Race is completed in a faster time.

6. What was the reason why Oxford lost the 2012 Boat Race?

   A   One of the rowers in the Oxford boat broke an oar.

   B   The umpire disqualified the Oxford boat.

   C   Disruption caused by a swimmer gave Cambridge an unfair advantage.

   D   Oxford only had seven men in their boat.

7. Which of the following is not mentioned in the text?

   A   When the first women's Boat Race was held.

   B   The winner of the 2012 men's Boat Race.

   C   The record time taken for a women's crew to complete the Tideway course.

   D   The number of men's Boat Races that have been held.

Find the word that means the same, or nearly the same, as the word on the left.

   Example: **wide**   flat   straight   <u>broad</u>   long

---

8. **simple**   prime   raw   primitive   unfinished

9. **breakage**   divide   disagreement   fracture   shattered

10. **bewitch**   transfix   immobilise   incapacitate   sorcery

11. **increase**   dilute augment oscillate condense

12. **defect**   blemish inadequacy restraint deficit

13. **innocent**   truthful flawless candid irreproachable

Three of the words in each list are linked. Mark the word that is not related to these three.

Example: journal diary <u>textbook</u> notebook

14. flash shutter lens photo

15. fictional spectral mythical imaginary

16. defeat conquer torture vanquish

17. donor charity contributor benefactor

18. ballet waltz salsa dance

19. sorrow solitude melancholy grief

20. separate extricate liberate release

END OF TEST

/ 20

You have **10 minutes** to do this test. Work as quickly and as accurately as you can.

Choose the correct words to complete the passage below.

Unicorns feature in many myths and legends

1. ☐ during
    ☐ throughout
    ☐ around
    ☐ over

history, with stories about

unicorn-like creatures

2. ☐ appear
    ☐ dating
    ☐ range
    ☐ emanate

back as far as Ancient Greece.

Descriptions of what unicorns looked like

3. ☐ differs
    ☐ digress
    ☐ contradicts
    ☐ vary

depending on which

4. ☐ sketches
    ☐ instructions
    ☐ accounts
    ☐ sheets

you read. Most early texts

5. ☐ say
    ☐ depict
    ☐ tell
    ☐ portray

of a wild animal with a long

horn on its head. It wasn't

6. ☐ after
    ☐ until
    ☐ to
    ☐ prior

medieval times that the description of a horse-like

animal, as we know unicorns today,

7. ☐ weren't
    ☐ turned
    ☐ became
    ☐ remain

widely accepted. During this period,

unicorns were

8. ☐ valued
    ☐ thought
    ☐ legend
    ☐ revere

for their magical qualities. The unicorn horn was thought to

115

9. ☐ shape
be made of a magic   ☐ materials   that could
  ☐ substance
  ☐ structure

10. ☐ cure
☐ recover   many diseases. There
☐ spread
☐ healing

is evidence that people bought narwhal tusks for medicinal

11. ☐ reason
☐ purposes, believing
☐ causes
☐ treats

them to be unicorn horns.

12. ☐ thought
Today, though most people   ☐ disagree   that unicorns are fictitious, they still appear in
  ☐ decide
  ☐ believe

popular culture.

Complete the word on the right so that it means the opposite,
or nearly the opposite, of the word on the left.

Example: heavy   l i g h t

13. disloyal   d ☐ v ☐ t ☐ ☐

14. conform   d ☐ s o ☐ ☐ y

15. crowded   ☐ e s ☐ ☐ t e d

16. stiff   p ☐ i ☐ n t

Mark the word outside the brackets that has a similar meaning to the words in both sets of brackets.

Example: (twig   branch)   (fasten   attach)   glue   <u>stick</u>   affix   bough

17. (behaviour   manner)   (manage   direct)   action   oversee   bearing   conduct

18. (hire   recruit)   (utilise   implement)   apply   employ   commission   use

19. (meeting   visit)   (era   time)   date   period   rendezvous   fixture

20. (series   sequence)   (tether   fasten)   tie   trail   chain   string

21. (impartial   neutral)   (target   aim)   end   just   objective   intention

Three of the words in each list are linked. Mark the word that is not related to these three.

Example: journal   diary   <u>textbook</u>   notebook

22. scarlet   cerise   turquoise   vermilion

23. momentary   transient   fleeting   diminutive

24. warrior   army   soldier   combatant

25. jackdaw   crow   sparrow   raven

26. favourable   conducive   beneficial   educational

END OF TEST

/ 26

Time for a break! These puzzles are a great way to practise your **vocabulary** skills.

Sorting Stars

Rearrange the words below so they spell out adjectives associated with stars. Then write the first letter of each word you've created in the corresponding numbered box. The correct letters will give the answer to the joke!

_____   _____

What's an astronaut's favourite drink?

| 2 | 3 | a | v | i | 4 | e | 1 | ! |

Where Am I?

Lucy, Tina and Paul are playing hide-and-seek in town.
Solve the clues below to work out where each of them are hiding.

Lucy: I am hidden somewhere that's
a synonym for 'advertise'.   __ __ __ __ __ __

Tina: I am hidden somewhere that can
mean 'treasury' or 'lakeshore'.   __ __ __ __

Paul: I am hidden somewhere that
rhymes with the antonym for 'light'.   __ __ __ __